PHYSICAL GEOGRAPHY

FOR CERTIFICATE STUDENTS

PHYSICAL GEOGRAPHY

FOR CERTIFICATE STUDENTS

H. R. CAIN, M.A.
Head of the Geography Department,
Alderman Newton's School, Leicester

LONGMANS

LONGMANS, GREEN AND CO LTD
48 Grosvenor Street, London W.1

*Associated companies, branches and representatives
throughout the world*

© H. R. CAIN, 1961
FIRST PUBLISHED 1961
SIXTH IMPRESSION 1966

PRINTED AND BOUND IN GREAT BRITAIN BY
HAZELL WATSON AND VINEY LTD
AYLESBURY, BUCKS

Preface

THE present volume sets out to describe the processes which are involved in the formation of man's environment and the physical features which result. In doing this, I have sought continually to remind the reader that, apart from the intrinsic interest of the physical environment, description of it is a necessary preliminary to an understanding of man's life and work upon the surface of the earth.

The material covered is that required in answering the questions on Physical Geography in the 'O' Level papers of the General Certificate of Education of the chief examining bodies. A selection of such questions appears at the end of the book. Some topics have been simplified rather more than is usual, as I believe that in the case of climate, for example (with which most pupils find difficulty), a sound but simple basis is of more importance at this stage than a welter of detail. I have not, however, hesitated to introduce any modern or advanced ideas which stimulate thought and promote discussion.

My sincere thanks are due to all those who have helped in the production of the book; to Professor F. J. Monkhouse, who has at all times been generous in affording me the benefit of his judgment and experience; to Mr. A. Carson Clark, Mr. R. M. Smethurst and Mr. P. R. Pople, who have drawn for me almost all of the diagrams; to Miss M. D. Roberts, late Assistant Librarian of Aerofilms, Ltd.; to Mr. A. H. Brown and to Malcolm and Joyce Liddle, who read through the text and made many helpful suggestions; and lastly to my wife, who has so willingly allowed herself to become involved in the incidentals of composition and preparation.

Leicester, 1961.   H. R. C.

Contents

CHAPTER ONE

What is Physical Geography?

THE Geography which is taught in schools today is a comparatively new subject. If you had been at school forty or fifty years ago, in what geographers nowadays call 'the bad old days of capes and bays', you would probably have spent most of your time learning by heart long lists of the highest mountains, the longest rivers and the largest towns. Only the other day a lady recited to the author a list of 'wool' towns that she had learnt as a child. When you left school, you would, if you had not been thoroughly bored by it all, have been a walking encyclopaedia of information about lengths and sizes of rivers and mountains, but you would have known very little about the various peoples of the world, their daily lives, their food, their work and their problems.

The Ancient Greeks, who were so wise and so far ahead of their time in many ways, took a very lively interest in all these things. They did not, however, call this kind of study 'Geography'. In fact, one of the first real Geography books is called a 'history'. It was written in the fifth century B.C. by a rich Greek named Herodotus, who travelled widely throughout the Mediterranean world and described the way of life of the peoples he had met and amongst whom he had lived. The important point about Herodotus is that he did not merely *describe*, he attempted to *explain*.

Over 2,000 years were to elapse before this attitude to life and work upon the surface of the earth was to reappear. The Romans were principally interested in registering places and distances on maps as an aid to military conquest, and throughout the Dark Ages Geography was just forgotten. The discoveries of the Elizabethan Age revealed many strange and distant lands, but for about the next 300 years everyone was so preoccupied with the mere amassing of knowledge, with seeking out openings for trade and colonisation and making maps that they had very little time or inclination to ponder on the significance of all the new facts that came crowding in upon them.

It was not until the last part of the nineteenth century that very much thought was given to the why and wherefore behind all this new body of knowledge—and only then by a few more enlightened thinkers. Eventually Geography on modern lines became recognised as a subject of study at the Universities, but in many schools the old Geography, which valued the acquisition of knowledge of facts and figures about places and products as an end in itself, still lingered on.

We often talk about going to some other part of the country 'for a change'. If you live in a third-storey flat in a big city, you

FIG. 1—Blocks of modern flats in a closely built-up area of London. Paddington railway station can be seen beyond the flats.

Aerofilms

FIG. 2—An old farmhouse in a lonely area of the northern Pennines.

lead a very different kind of life on holiday in the country or at the seaside. And, of course, if you go abroad, the change in your way of life and your scenery and surroundings is even greater. It is these differences in the way of life of people in different parts of the world or even in different parts of the same country that we are trying to discover in modern Geography (compare Fig. 1 and Fig. 2).

The kind of life that people lead is to a large extent controlled by all those things which make up what geographers call their *environment*. For instance, the climate decides the kind of clothes you wear, the design of the house in which you live, and even the games you play. The rocks which form the earth's surface help to decide the kind of soil and the type of farming in your district, and this may in turn decide the sort of food you eat. In some parts of the world this is much more important than it is in Europe, where roads and railways and modern transport facilities make it possible to trade with other lands, and thus to buy foods and drinks which Nature does not allow us to produce at home. If you live in the centre of a big city, you may go to school just round the corner, but in the north of Scotland you may have to tramp for miles across the moors to get there. Moreover, if you live in a town like Bradford or Leicester, you will probably think, when you leave school, of getting work in a textile factory or an engineering works; but if you live in Cornwall, you are more likely to become a farmer or a fisherman, because your surroundings or environment are different in each place.

Of course, you are not forced to live the kind of life your environment suggests. You can, if you wish, move to another

FIG. 3—Fen country near Boston in Lincolnshire. This was once a region of useless swamp. The Forty-Foot Level shown on the picture and various other canals which have been dug to drain away the excess water have turned it into a highly productive agricultural area.

Aerofilms

town or another country; you can, as the geographer says, 'control your environment' by digging canals, for example, to bring water to land which Nature has denied sufficient rainfall, by building aircraft to cross deserts which have previously been unconquerable, by carrying tropical fruits to temperate lands in airtight tins or refrigerator ships, or by flood-lighting foot-ball grounds so that matches can be played after dark. A further example is shown in Fig. 3.

Since Geography is the study of man's life and work in relation to his environment, we must obviously first study this environment. This study is called *Physical Geography*.

CHAPTER TWO

The Rocks of the Earth's Surface

WE may conveniently begin our description of the physical environment with the solid rock which lies beneath our feet. Most people think of rocks as necessarily hard, heavy and resistant, and would be very surprised to hear the sand on the beach or the soft mud at the bottom of a river so described. The geologist and geographer, however, class as rocks all the solid materials of which the earth's crust is composed, whether sandstone, granite, clay, chalk, gravel or mud.

The various kinds of rocks differ widely from each other in colour, density, texture and their ability to resist erosion, and also in the methods by which they have been formed by Nature. Since, however, there are three chief ways in which the rocks of the crust have been made, it is usually convenient to divide them into three large groups on this basis.

1. SEDIMENTARY ROCKS

Rivers and streams wear away or *erode* particles from the rocks over which they pass and carry them along in the moving water. When they reach the comparatively quiet waters of the sea, these particles fall to the bottom. On the floors of the seas and oceans vast areas are carpeted by layers of deposited material or *sediment* brought down by the rivers. As more and more material is added, the particles underneath are pressed more tightly together and the moisture is squeezed out. If deposition goes on in this way for a sufficiently long period without being disturbed, the sediment may reach a thickness of hundreds of feet (Fig. 4). Rocks formed from sediments laid down under water are called sedimentary rocks.

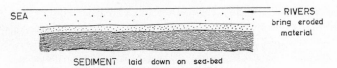

FIG. 4—The formation of sedimentary rock.

Sedimentary rocks have three important characteristics:

(i) *They are laid down in layers or strata.* It may be that after a time the type of eroded material brought down to the sea will alter. Some minor earth-movement may, for instance, cause a river to change its course and so carry to the sea particles of a different nature. This may happen several times before the sea becomes dry land, and the rocks will accordingly appear in layers of different character. Each of these layers is called by the geologist a *stratum** (Fig. 5). The surface where one stratum

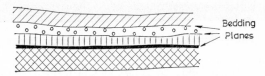

FIG. 5—Strata and bedding planes.

lies upon another is the *bedding plane.* Strata of different rocks can often be seen in cliffs at the seaside, in railway cuttings and in quarries (Fig. 6). Some of them may be many feet in thickness, while others may be only a few inches. The thickness of the stratum gives a rough indication of the length of time during which conditions remained the same.

Some of the strata may have bands or layers within themselves—but in this case probably only one hundredth of an inch thick. These are known as *laminae.*† They make a stratum look like a pile of sheets of paper, and represent slight changes in

* The plural of *stratum* is *strata.*
† *Lamina* is Latin for 'leaf'. The plural is *laminae.*

FIG. 6—Stratified rocks at Worbarrow Tout in Dorset.

conditions, or possibly the stages by which the whole stratum is gradually built up. In a pile of books on the table the books themselves would represent the strata and the leaves of the books the laminae (Fig. 7).

(ii) *They may contain fossils.* When various creatures or plants which lived in the sea in bygone ages died, their remains sank to the bottom and were covered by sediment. The fleshy parts rotted away, but their skeletons usually remained long enough for sediments to harden around them. The impressions formed in the rock in this way are called *fossils*. The detail in these impressions is quite remarkable, but sometimes Nature is even more obliging. In certain circumstances the substance of which the original organism was composed has been replaced particle by particle by some other substance, which did not decompose in the course of time. One can find fossilised logs made of opal,

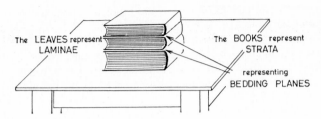

Fig. 7—Laminae in relation to strata.

a shiny, highly coloured rock. Every tiny fragment of the wood right to the centre of the log has been replaced by an equally tiny fragment of opal, so that every detail of the original wood has been preserved. In rocks formed only a short time ago, from the geological point of view, there are sometimes found the actual bones, teeth and tusks of prehistoric animals whose bodies fell into the water and were covered by sediments. These too are called fossils.

Two typical fossils are shown in Fig. 8.

(iii) *They are not crystalline.* Certain substances, such as washing soda and Epsom salts, are made of crystals—shiny,

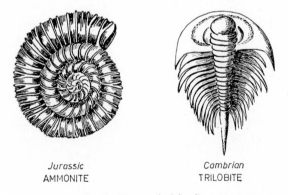

Jurassic
AMMONITE

Cambrian
TRILOBITE

Fig. 8—Two typical fossils.

regular shapes all more or less the same size. Crystals will be discussed in greater detail in connection with the second large group of rocks, but for the moment it is sufficient to note that a sedimentary rock is not made up of crystals. Some of the particles of eroded material of which it consists may however have come from fragments of broken crystals carried along by moving water and rounded off in the process but, generally speaking, a sedimentary rock has a dull appearance and does not reflect the light.

Types of Sedimentary Rocks. (*a*) *Mechanically formed.* It would be impossible to describe all the various kinds of sedi-

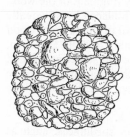

Fig. 9—A lump of conglomerate or 'pudding-stone' (about ⅓ full size).

mentary rocks which have been formed by the piling up of particles derived from other rocks, but there are certain very common ones about which everybody should know something.

Conglomerate consists of masses of pebbles stuck together by a cement of very fine particles (Fig. 9). It must originally have been a bed of shingle such as you find on many seashores, and since it so resembles a piece of 'plum pudding', it is often called pudding-stone.

Sandstones are like the conglomerate, but the constituents are on a much smaller scale, and in place of pebbles are grains of sand. Sandstones vary enormously. Some can be sawn quite easily into blocks for building; these are called freestones. Some split easily into slabs and are referred to as flagstones. They vary, too, in colour; there is the Greensand of Kent and the Old Red Sandstone of Scotland, for example.

Clays are made up of even smaller particles than the sandstones. For thousands of years clay has been used for making bricks and tiles, but it has many other uses. One special kind of clay, called fireclay, is able to resist intense heat, and is therefore used to line the insides of furnaces. Another kind, *kaolin* or china-clay, formed as a result of the decomposition of granite

Aerofilms

FIG. 10—China-clay workings near St. Austell in Cornwall. China-clay is formed from the decomposed crystals of felspar in granite. The coarser, unwanted fragments of sand are separated in water from the particles of china-clay and dumped in great heaps as shown in the picture.

in situ, is used in pottery, gives paper a smooth surface, and is one of the ingredients of toothpaste (Fig. 10).

(*b*) *Organically formed.* Rocks formed from the remains of living things are known as organic rocks. Certain tiny creatures which live in the sea create for themselves shells from the calcium carbonate which they take from the sea water. When they die these shells, or parts of them, accumulate on the sea bed in very much the same way as the particles which make up sandstones and clays, forming limestone. Some kinds of plants also are able to secrete calcium carbonate, and they too build up beds of organic rock.

There are many different types of limestone in various parts of the world, but two are of especial importance in the geography of the British Isles. *Carboniferous limestone* (so called because it was formed in that period to which geologists have given the name 'Carboniferous') is found in the Pennines, for example, and gives rise to some very peculiar features in the scenery of the district. A great band of *oolitic limestone* stretches across England from near Scarborough to Portland Bill, and consists of masses of rock which look like myriads of pin heads stuck together. This is a valuable source of iron-ore.

Chalk, which forms the North and South Downs of Kent and Sussex, Beachy Head near Eastbourne and the white cliffs of Dover, is another form of limestone (Fig. 11).

Carbonaceous* rocks form a very important group of organic rocks. These have been built up from the stems, roots and leaves of plants which grew in tropical swamps, compressed by layers of clay laid down on top of them. Gradually most of the other things (such as oxygen and nitrogen) which made up the original plants were driven off and more or less pure carbon was left behind, forming what we know as *coal*. *Lignite* is softer than ordinary household coal, grey in colour, and geologically younger. *Anthracite* is harder and shinier, and gives out more heat than the other kinds of coal.

(*c*) *Chemically formed*. Ordinary table salt is made from *rock salt*, which is found as a sedimentary rock on the beds of certain seas and lakes, and in strata among the solid rocks, and is formed as a result of chemical processes. The water of the sea is sometimes unable to dissolve all the salt it contains, and the surplus salt is deposited on the bottom. *Gypsum*, or to give it its chemical name of calcium sulphate, is deposited in the same way, and large quantities of it are found on the bed of the Dead Sea.

* Distinguish carefully between *carboniferous* and *carbonaceous*.

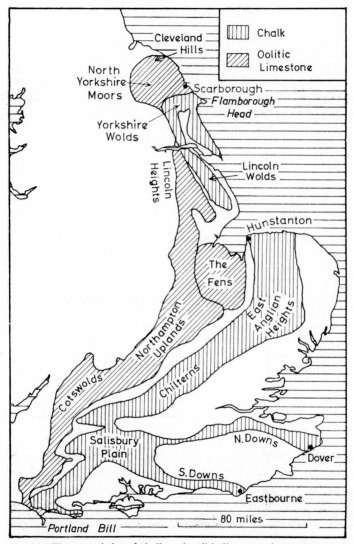

Fig. 11—The great belts of chalk and oolitic limestone in southern and eastern England. Some parts of these belts rise as lines of low hills (called escarpments), while others are covered by later materials, such as alluvium, peat or glacial deposits.

2. IGNEOUS ROCKS

The Latin word *ignis* means 'fire', and this gives us a clue to the meaning of 'igneous' rocks, the second large group into which the rocks of the earth's crust are divided. Molten material sometimes forces its way up from beneath the crust in volcanic eruptions. The rocks which are formed when this material from inside the earth cools down and solidifies at or just below the surface are known as igneous rocks. Fire, or at any rate heat, is as essential in the formation of igneous rocks as water is in the formation of sedimentary rocks.

We obviously cannot expect to find the igneous rocks laid down in strata, and it would be absurd to suppose that they might contain fossils. The chief characteristic which enables us to recognise them is that they are *crystalline*.

The atoms which make up many of the substances found in Nature have the property, under certain circumstances, of arranging themselves in groups forming a definite pattern. This pattern produces in the case of each of these substances a particular geometrical shape which is repeated over and over again; these little shapes are called *crystals* (Fig. 12). When the molten material from deep in the earth cools down, the various chemical compounds or *minerals* of which it is composed tend to form crystals. If it is allowed to cool down very slowly, the atoms have plenty of time to arrange themselves in patterns, and comparatively large crystals are formed in the rock. If it cools down at only a moderate rate, the crystals are

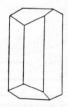

FIG 12—Typical rock-forming crystals (very greatly magnified).

smaller; but if cooling is rapid, the rock solidifies while the atoms are all jumbled up, and presents, therefore, a glassy appearance.

Types of Igneous Rocks. Igneous rocks are classified by the geologist both by their chemical composition and by the depth at which they solidified. Those which reached the surface and cooled down quickly, before the crystals could form properly, are known as volcanic rocks or *lava*. If they contain a large proportion of silica, they are described as *acid*; these have been derived from viscous (that is thick, sticky) material which flowed very slowly. If they contain little silica, they are said to be *basic*; these were originally non-viscous or 'runny' material which flowed probably for miles before it solidified. *Basalt* is an example of a volcanic rock. The great six-sided pillars which form the famous Giant's Causeway in Northern Ireland and Fingal's Cave in the island of Staffa off the west coast of Scotland are made of basalt.

The igneous rocks which solidified at intermediate depths are called *hypabyssal* rocks, and appear to have cooled down in the course of their journey to the surface. In some cases they forced their way into existing gaps in the sedimentary layers, and in others they forced the strata apart and filled the spaces they had themselves made. Such rocks are described as intrusive (see p. 40).

Those which solidified at great depths are classed as *plutonic* rocks (from Pluto, the god of the Underworld). Since plutonic rocks cooled down quite slowly, the various minerals they contain are found in crystalline form. Almost all the many different kinds of granite show this clearly. If you have a piece of Dartmoor granite, for instance, you will be able to see in it pink crystals of felspar (a mineral with a very complicated chemical formula) and black crystals of mica embedded in a glass-like substance which is actually crystalline quartz. The crystals of quartz are so tiny that you will not be able to see them separately without a special geological microscope, but the crystals of felspar and mica, which are shaped as shown in Fig. 13, are easily picked out. The crystals of felspar and mica embedded in

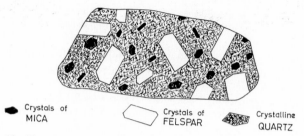

FIG. 13—The polished face of a piece of Dartmoor granite (about ⅓ full size).

the mass of quartz may possibly remind you of the conglomerate. But here there are definite geometrical shapes in place of pebbles, and the whole rock is crystalline in form.

Igneous rocks are nearly always very hard, and they are, therefore, in great demand for purposes where toughness is the chief consideration—for making and mending roads, for instance. Large quantities of igneous rock are quarried for road metal near Penmaenmawr (Fig. 14) and Conway in North Wales and in the Charnwood Forest area of Leicestershire. They often show very attractive mottling when highly polished, and for this reason, as well as their durability, they are used for gravestones, monuments and public buildings.

3. METAMORPHIC ROCKS

The word 'igneous' came from Latin: 'metamorphic' comes from Greek, and means 'changing form'. This is precisely what has happened to metamorphic rocks. Originally they were either sedimentary or igneous rocks, but since the time they were formed as such, something has occurred to change them. We sometimes find rocks laid down in strata, but crystalline in form. The cause of the change is usually that a sedimentary rock has been subjected to such intense heat that it has melted without moving from its position, and as it slowly cooled down again, the minerals arranged themselves in crystals. This could

Aerofilms

FIG. 14—Quarrying the igneous rocks near Penmaenmawr in North Wales
for road metal.

easily happen when molten material poured over existing rocks or forced its way into cracks (Fig. 15).

Sometimes immense pressure is also involved. *Slate* is a metamorphic rock which was originally clay. Heat and pressure have flattened out all the particles in the clay, so that now they all lie parallel to one another. The way in which they are

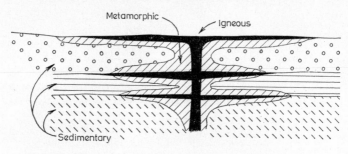

FIG. 15—Metamorphic rocks formed by contact-metamorphism.

arranged makes the rock very easy to split into thin plates or sheets which are very suitable for roofing houses.

Marble is another metamorphic rock, formed by the metamorphism of limestone.

Many of these 'changed' rocks clearly resemble igneous rocks to a great extent and are used for similar purposes. The Lizard Peninsula in the south of Cornwall consists partly of a dark green rock called *serpentine*. Many of the shops in the district display for sale pieces of this rock shaped and polished on lathes to represent lighthouses and labelled 'A Souvenir from the Lizard'.

4. CLASSIFICATION OF THE ROCKS BY AGE

The foregoing classification of the rocks of the earth's surface is quite satisfactory as far as it goes. It takes into account their mode of formation and to some extent their chemical composition, but it tells us little or nothing about their relative ages.

The Geological Map. In the case of sedimentary rocks it is obvious that we may expect to find the older rocks underneath the newer ones, and if all the various kinds of sedimentary rocks had been laid down in one place, we could immediately draw up a neat little pile of rectangles, each coloured to represent a particular kind of rock, to illustrate the sequence.

In your atlas there is almost certainly a geological map of the British Isles, looking rather like a gaily coloured patchwork quilt. At the side of the map is a key consisting of a pile of rectangles, and against each is the name given to the rocks of that particular age. But since the complete sequence from top to bottom does not occur anywhere in the world, let alone in the British Isles, you may well wonder how it was possible to construct such a table at all. It is, in fact, the result of a great deal of patient detective work by geologists among the fossils that the rocks contain.

The Evidence of the Fossils. Wherever it was possible to examine the fossils through any considerable depth of rocks, it was found that the deepest—and therefore presumably the oldest—rocks contained fossils of simpler organisms than the rocks above. Some of the very earliest rocks were found to contain, for instance, fossils of sea-creatures called trilobites (Fig. 8); later rocks contained fossils of fishes and birds, followed by those of reptiles and land animals more or less resembling creatures of today. If a layer of rocks in one place displayed the same kind of fossils as a layer somewhere else, it was assumed that the two layers were laid down at about the same time.

Gradually the scattered pieces of the 'jig-saw puzzle' were fitted together, and so the time-scale which accompanies the geological map was built up. It is now possible to tell the age of a layer of rock merely by noting the type of fossils it contains. Small wonder that so many pages in geological text-books are devoted to detailed descriptions of fossils, or that the names given to the three main divisions of the classification of rocks by time make reference to the history of life upon the earth's surface. The words *Palaeozoic*, *Mesozoic* and *Cainozoic* are derived from Greek and mean 'ancient life', 'middle life' and 'new life' respectively. The names of the sub-divisions—the *periods* or *systems*—come from various sources; some from Greek, some from the names of mountains, and some from the names given by the Romans to tribes who inhabited areas in which those particular types of rock are found. The complete table of geological periods is shown in Fig. 16. It would, of course, be quite impossible to adopt the same method in classifying igneous and metamorphic rocks, since they contain no fossils.

The first geological map of England and Wales was published in 1815 by a surveyor and civil engineer named William Smith. He became interested in the rocks in the course of his work as a canal builder and is said to have travelled 10,000 miles in a year in preparing his map.

What is Shown on the Map. The geological map shows the solid rock which appears at the surface, or *outcrops*, if we ignore the soil and any 'drift' deposits (see p. 109) which may have been laid down on top. For these, special maps are usually available. In addition to the age of the rocks as shown by the period to which they belong, some indication will also be given of their nature according to the previous classification— whether they are formed of sandstone, clay, chalk, limestone, etc. Apart from the fact that older rocks tend to be harder and more resistant than recent rocks, there is no obvious connection between the age of a rock and its nature or mode of origin.

What the Rocks Reveal. Climatic and other conditions are known to have changed as the periods succeeded one another, and if we remember the conditions which prevailed in each of the periods, we can by inference gather something of the manner in which the rocks of any particular period were laid down, and hence their nature. To take but a few examples, it is thought that in Devonian times much of what we now call the British Isles consisted of desert, which has given the very distinct red colour to the Old Red Sandstone deposits of parts of Somerset and Devon. The desert was then inundated in the Carboni-

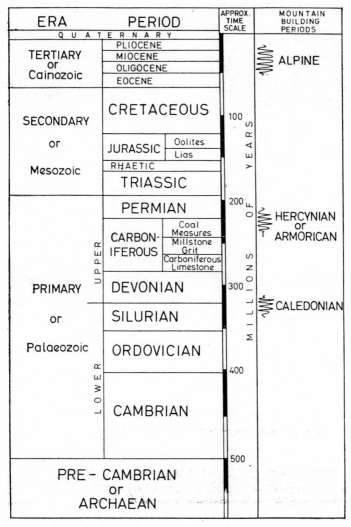

ERA	PERIOD		APPROX. TIME SCALE	MOUNTAIN BUILDING PERIODS
	QUATERNARY			
TERTIARY or Cainozoic	PLIOCENE			ALPINE
	MIOCENE			
	OLIGOCENE			
	EOCENE			
SECONDARY or Mesozoic	CRETACEOUS		100	
	JURASSIC	Oolites		
		Lias		
	RHAETIC			
	TRIASSIC			
PRIMARY or Palaeozoic	PERMIAN		200	HERCYNIAN or ARMORICAN
	CARBON-IFEROUS (UPPER)	Coal Measures		
		Millstone Grit		
		Carboniferous Limestone		
	DEVONIAN (UPPER)		300	
	SILURIAN (LOWER)			CALEDONIAN
	ORDOVICIAN (LOWER)		400	
	CAMBRIAN (LOWER)			
			500	
PRE - CAMBRIAN or ARCHAEAN				

(MILLIONS OF YEARS)

Fig. 16—Table of geological periods—the rocks classified by age.

ferous period by a tropical sea, in which limestone was laid down. A river flowing from a land mass somewhere to the north next proceeded to build up in the sea an enormous delta consisting of a coarse kind of sandstone called millstone grit.*
The area finally turned into a swamp in which grew the plants that were eventually to become seams of coal. In Cretaceous times a tropical sea once again covered most of the 'British Isles', and it was not until Tertiary (or Cainozoic) times that a land surface appeared at all resembling that of today. Throughout the first part of the Quaternary era extremely cold conditions prevailed, and much of this land surface lay under a great thickness of ice.

Paradoxical as it may seem, it is by studying the rocks themselves that geologists have been able to find out about these changes of climate and scenery.

The patchwork appearance of the geological map is due to the fact that so much has happened to these layers of rock since they were originally laid down. All but the youngest have been buried by succeeding layers and now appear at the surface only where the covering rocks have been worn away. Nearly all have at some time been cracked, tilted and bent by movements in the earth's crust, and the map represents the planed-off surface of the underlying disorder.

* So called because circular slabs of the rock were at one time used for grinding corn.

CHAPTER THREE

Our Unstable Earth

THE surface features of the earth are of as much importance to the geographer as the nature of the rocks, and although running water, wind and ice are for ever reshaping, modifying, destroying and rebuilding these surface features, the forces which give them their original outlines operate within the earth itself. It is, therefore, necessary for us to examine as best we can that part of the earth which lies beneath the crust or *lithosphere*, and the internal forces which affect it.

THE INTERIOR OF THE EARTH

If you were to go down a very deep hole, such as the shaft of a mine, taking with you a thermometer, you would find that the temperature would rise about 1° F. for every 60 feet you went down. It does not require much imagination (or calculation) to see that by the time you had gone two miles down, you would have reached the temperature at which water boils. And there would still be nearly 4,000 miles to go before you reached the centre of the earth! If the temperature goes on rising at this same rate all the way to the centre (it may do, but we are not quite sure), you would not get very far before you arrived at a point at which the temperature was capable of melting the very rocks of which the earth is composed. If you went down still farther, the heat would be so great that we should expect ordinary rocks to be turned into gas.

Actually, scientists are quite certain that the centre of the earth is not gas, although the heat is so great that theoretically it should be. They tell us that it is most likely that the centre of the earth is composed of a mixture of nickel and iron, and that the enormous weight of the outer layers pressing downwards prevents the centre from turning to a liquid, let alone a gas. They admit, however, that it may be slightly 'waxy' in consistency.

Fortunately, there are some parts of the earth where the temperature does not rise quite so rapidly as we go downwards. In South Africa, for instance, it is possible for diamond miners to work two miles below the surface.

MOVEMENTS IN THE EARTH'S CRUST

Horizontal Movements. Not so very many years ago it was discovered that the great continental land masses are composed of quite different rocks from the beds of the oceans. The continents are formed of comparatively light rocks to which the geologists have given the name *sial* (from *si*licon and *al*uminium), and the ocean beds of what they call *sima* (from *si*licon and *ma*gnesium), and they suggest that the large 'slabs' of sial which form the continents are resting on, or even floating in, a layer of sima covering the whole earth (Fig. 17).

These 'slabs' of sial have not necessarily always occupied the position on the face of the earth that they do now. In 1912 a German named Wegener suggested that at one time there were two very large patches of sial, one in the northern hemisphere, called Laurasia, and another, called Gondwanaland, in the

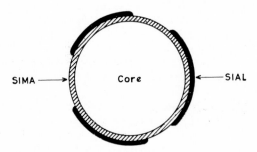

FIG. 17—Sial and sima.

southern hemisphere, and that they subsequently split into smaller pieces which 'floated' apart. These pieces form 'shields' of very old, hard rock, which now make up most of Africa, the western half of Australia, the northern part of Canada, and a number of other areas (Fig. 18).

We must not let ourselves suppose that such movements as this took place suddenly, as it were overnight. The break-up of Gondwanaland probably took millions of years to complete, but, compared with the hundreds of millions of years that have elapsed since then, the event may be thought of as comparatively swift. Some geologists think that Africa at this moment is 'splitting down the middle', and that the two halves are 'drifting' apart.

Vertical Movements. Long before anyone dreamed that parts of the earth's crust might be capable of moving sideways, it was known that parts of it could move up or down.

Raised Beaches. You can see the evidence for yourself if you go, for instance, to certain parts of Scotland or Norway. There you can find places where the sea is breaking against a cliff face, and at the top of the cliff can be seen what has clearly been a beach, with sand and shingle and another line of cliffs behind them (Fig. 19). These features are called raised beaches, and it seems reasonable to suppose that these particular areas of the earth's surface have risen. It could be, of course, that the level of the sea has fallen, but from other clues to the problem we can tell that this is extremely unlikely.

Submerged Forests. There are places off the shores of Britain where you can find remains of forests under the sea. These submerged forests are an indication that the land has sunk. Old legends, however, about Lyonesse—a sort of extension of Cornwall under the sea—and similar stories of bells ringing from churches buried under lakes are certainly little more than fairy tales. Nothing quite as spectacular as this is likely to have happened in the comparatively short space of time in which men have been able to build churches.

Folding. If you look at a physical map of the world, you will notice long lines of high mountains such as the Himalayas, the

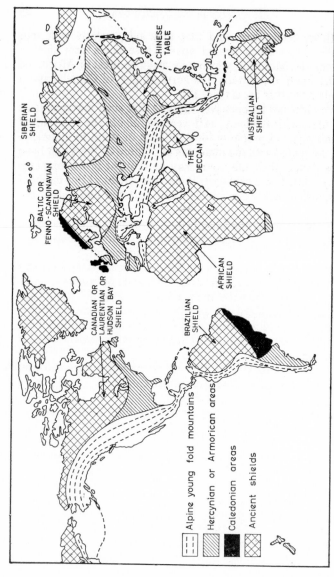

FIG. 18—Structural divisions of the world (simplified).

SIBERIAN SHIELD

CHINESE TABLE

AUSTRALIAN SHIELD

THE DECCAN

BALTIC OR FENNO-SCANDINAVIAN SHIELD

CANADIAN OR LAURENTIAN OR HUDSON BAY SHIELD

AFRICAN SHIELD

BRAZILIAN SHIELD

Alpine young fold mountains

Hercynian or Armorican areas

Caledonian areas

Ancient shields

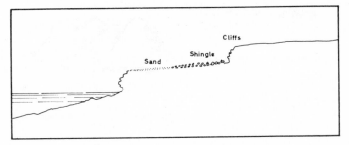

FIG. 19—Section across a raised beach.

Rockies, the Andes and the Alps. These are examples of young fold mountains, and at a rough guess about forty million years ago the earth went through a period when parts of the crust wrinkled like a tablecloth when you push it from one end of the table. It used to be thought that this was caused by the earth shrinking as it cooled down. We are not so sure nowadays about the reason for the shrinking, but it is fairly obvious that during this period, which probably lasted several million years, a great upheaval did take place. Some of the shields mentioned above were tilted, volcanoes poured out masses of lava, and long lines of mountains were formed. This is called the *Alpine mountain building period*, and was the third such mountain building period of which we can find traces in the materials of the earth's crust. The first—that is, the earliest—is given the name *Caledonian*, because the mountains of northern Scotland (the Roman 'Caledonia') were originally formed at that time. The second is named *Hercynian*, after the Harz Mountains of Germany (Fig. 18).

The Hercynian and Caledonian mountains are not so easy to detect by looking at the physical map, but the scenery produced by each type of mountain is quite distinct. Fig. 20 shows the difference. The Alpine mountains are very high, and the skyline is jagged, like the teeth of a saw. In fact, the Spanish word *sierra* meaning 'saw' is often used in naming mountain chains (e.g. Sierra Morena, Sierra Nevada). The Hercynian and Cale-

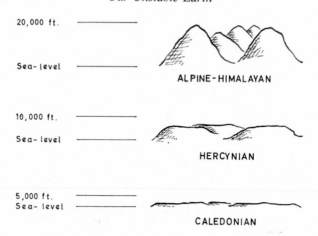

20,000 ft. ————————

Sea-level ————————

ALPINE-HIMALAYAN

10,000 ft. ————————

Sea-level ————————

HERCYNIAN

5,000 ft. ————————
Sea-level ————————

CALEDONIAN

FIG. 20—Typical sky-line of Alpine-Himalayan, Hercynian and Caledonian mountain regions.

donian mountains (Fig. 21) are lower and flatter, as if Nature had taken a huge file and worn them down. We need not for the moment concern ourselves with the processes by which the mountains are worn down and flattened, which will be dealt with in Chapter 4. The geological periods in which these great upheavals took place are shown in Fig. 16. There were probably still other mountain building periods before these, but most of their traces have been destroyed, so it is difficult to be quite sure.

Types of Folds. The crest of a fold is known as the *anticline* and the trough as the *syncline*, but in very few systems of folds is the arrangement of anticlines and synclines as symmetrical as the wrinkles in a tablecloth. Sometimes the crest is pushed so far over as to form an *overfold*, or even farther still, a *recumbent fold*. In extreme cases, such as may be found in the Alps, the rocks in a recumbent fold break, and the top half of the fold is pushed forward over the bottom half along a *thrust plane*, forming an *overthrust fold*. If it is overthrust still farther, it

Aerofilms

FIG. 21—The Grampian Mountains near Inverness. The uniform surface of the uplands is due to the fact that, after being folded in the Caledonian mountain building period, the area was worn down to a peneplain (see Chapter 4). It was subsequently uplifted wholesale, and the hollows shown in the picture have been carved out by streams after the uplift.

becomes a *nappe*, where the overlying rocks have broken away, and are separated by long distances from their 'roots'. Where the rocks are thrown up into an elongated dome rather than a fold, as in the Weald of Kent and Sussex, a *pericline* is formed. (Fig. 22).

Joints. The internal stresses set up by bending or folding tend to produce in a rock sets of cracks often so minute as to be almost imperceptible. These are known as joints, and usually run at right angles to each other, with one set parallel to the bedding plane or surface where one stratum lies upon another. In some rocks they are better developed than in others, since a

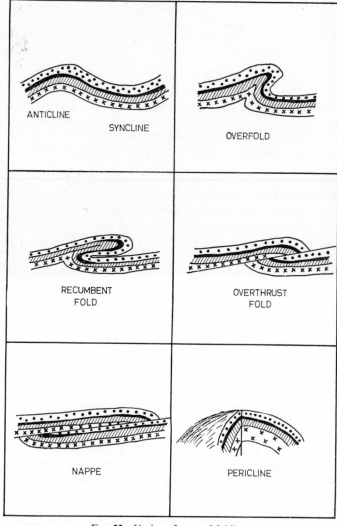

Fig. 22—Various forms of folding.

great deal depends on the nature of the rock. They are, in general, very useful to quarrymen who wish to split the rock into slabs or blocks.

Not all joints are formed by stress within the rock. Some are formed by the drying-out of sediments, and joints in igneous rocks are caused by cooling from the molten state.

Faulting. Not only can the crust of the earth bend; it can also crack. On geological maps *fault lines*, where the rocks have snapped under strain or pressure, are shown by lines with *f* written through them (Fig. 23).

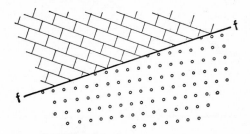

FIG. 23—Showing how a fault line is indicated on
a geological map.

Some fault lines are quite small, but the San Andreas Fault, running roughly through San Francisco and Los Angeles, is over 300 miles long. One of the best-known faults in Great Britain is the Pennine Fault, which overlooks Penrith and Appleby in the Eden Valley (Fig. 24). The two sides of a fault may slip sideways or up and down against each other (Fig. 25). Geologists can tell that this has happened by noting how a layer of a certain kind of rock suddenly ends at one side of the crack and is continued on the other side higher up. There may be no step-up at ground level, because the abrupt slope caused in the original movement has been smoothed off in the course of time. When a large number of faults runs across seams of coal, mining becomes extremely difficult.

Two faults sometimes occur parallel to each other, and if

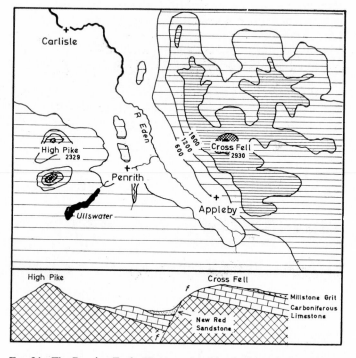

FIG. 24—The Pennine Fault. The cross-hatching indicates Lower Palaeozoic rocks.

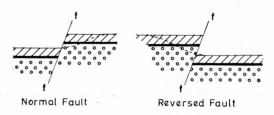

FIG. 25—Vertical sections through two kinds of faults.

the rocks between have slipped down to produce a kind of big trench, a *rift valley* is formed. This, together with other land forms caused by faulting, is shown in Fig. 26. A rift valley through which flows the River Rhine extends from Basle in Switzerland to Mainz in Germany, and in North Wales a shallow rift valley separates Anglesey from the mainland. From a point in the north of Ireland a number of fault lines radiate outwards to the north-east. Between two of these faults the land has sunk and now forms a rift valley which you will find marked on the map as the Midland Valley of Scotland or the Scottish Lowlands (Fig. 27. See also Fig. 28).

Actually, on each side of a rift valley there is very often a set of parallel faults, with the land surface descending to the floor of the valley by a series of steps. This is appropriately called *step-faulting*.

Close to the River Rhine are several 'blocks' or *horsts*, such

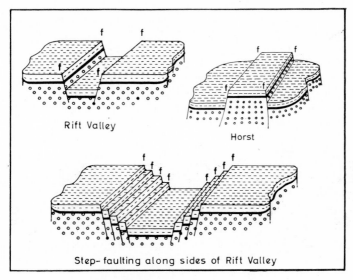

FIG. 26--Land forms caused by faulting.

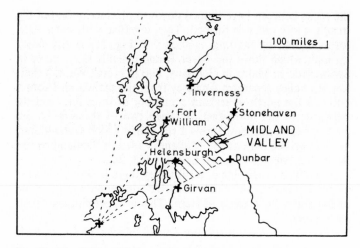

Fig. 27—The Midland Valley of Scotland. The land between two of the faults has sunk, thus forming an area of lowland in which most of the people of Scotland live.

as the Hunsrück Mountains (Fig. 29), the Vosges and the Black Forest, the steep sides of which have been formed partly by faulting. In the Lakeland of Central Sweden criss-cross faults have divided up the landscape so that it now resembles a very uneven slabbed pavement (see pp. 92–3).

VOLCANIC ACTIVITY

Those regions of the world in which young fold mountains are found appear to be the weakest parts of the earth's crust. The fold mountains themselves are one proof of this, but there are others, and it is here that we find most of the world's active volcanoes. We are all familiar with pictures of the famous ones like Vesuvius in Italy or Fujiyama in Japan, and we are apt to think that all volcanoes must be like these. There are, however, several different kinds.

FIG. 28—Glen More in Scotland, looking south-west. This is a fault line, along which a valley was gouged out and widened by ice (see Chap. 8). In the foreground is Loch Oich and in the distance Ben Nevis.

FIG. 29—The Rhine Gorge between Mainz and Bonn, showing on the left the Hunsrück horst. The steep slopes on either side of the Rhine are here due, not to faulting, but to down-cutting by the river as the land was slowly uplifted.

The Birth of a Volcano. There are few recorded accounts of anyone witnessing the actual birth of a volcano, but in 1943 a Mexican farmer while ploughing his field noticed a crack in the ground out of which smoke was rising as though from some underground fire. The smoke was followed by a gentle issue of ashes and lava, and the news of the phenomenon brought geologists from far and near hurrying to the spot. Within the space of a few weeks it became obvious that a volcano was being born, and by the time a year had elapsed the cone of Paricutin had grown to over a quarter of a mile in height.

Formation of the Cone. For reasons which we do not fully understand, it sometimes happens that molten rock or lava, together with steam and other gases, pushes its way up from deep down below the surface and overflows through a hole in the ground. If this lava is viscous, it cannot flow very far, but cools down and solidifies close to the vent, forming a cone like that of Vesuvius. But if the lava is non-viscous, it forms a very flat cone or spreads over the surrounding countryside in a vast sheet. In between the layers of lava which mark the various eruptions, layers of cinders and ashes (Fig. 30) will usually be found.

Types of Eruption. Some volcanoes, like Stromboli in the Lipari Islands off the north coast of Sicily, simmer gently all the time and erupt every hour or so. But in others, such as Vulcano, not far from Stromboli, the lava at the top of the pipe

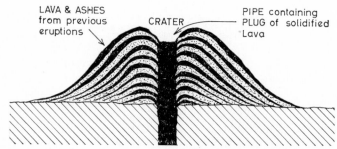

FIG. 30—Section through the cone of a typical volcano.

crusts over, forming a temporary plug. When sufficient pressure has been built up inside the volcano, a rather more violent explosion occurs. In the case of volcanoes like Vesuvius, the periods between eruptions are very much longer, the lava in the pipe solidifies to a greater depth, and the explosion, when it does occur, is still more violent. Bombs have at times been dropped from aircraft into volcanic craters in order to prevent too deep a crust from forming, and so touch off less violent explosions.

Sometimes the plug seals up the pipe so effectively that the lava finds it easier and more convenient to blow for itself another hole, by-passing the original vent. We may thus find a *parasitic cone* superimposed on the main cone (Fig. 31*a*). Etna in Sicily, which is the largest volcano in Europe, has hundreds of such parasitic cones. The volcano may even blow off its own head, leaving an enormous crater, in some cases several miles wide, known as a *caldera* (Fig. 31*b*). The three-mile-wide crater of Kilauea in the Hawaiian Islands still contains a number of pools of seething lava, while the Crater Lake in Oregon occupies a vast caldera six miles across, the relic of some former explosion.

One of the most terrible manifestations of volcanic fury is the *nuée ardente*, an explosive blast of incandescent gas charged with minute fragments of white-hot lava bursting from the side of a volcanic cone. In 1902 Mont Pelée in the island of Martinique erupted, and it was assumed that this burst of activity would follow the pattern of the two previous and comparatively mild eruptions in 1792 and 1851. But this time a *nuée ardente* of unparalleled violence burst over St. Pierre, the capital of

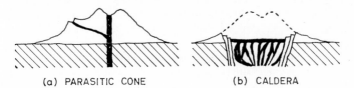

(a) PARASITIC CONE   (b) CALDERA

Fig. 31—A parasitic cone and a caldera.

Martinique, and all but two of its 28,000 inhabitants were instantly cremated as they sat at their office desks or restaurant tables. Of the two who escaped one was a woman who happened to be in the cellar at the time, and the other was a prisoner in an underground dungeon.

One might imagine that people would take great care not to live too close to a volcano in case it erupted. Fortunately, most volcanoes give some sort of warning when they are about to erupt in the form of preliminary tremors or subterranean rumblings. Moreover, the soils formed from the lava are usually so fertile that farms and villages are often situated dangerously near.

Products of Eruption. Apart from the lava which pours out of the vent, *volcanic bombs* of molten lava may be thrown high into the air, which solidify before they reach the ground. Fragments of shattered rock, steam and various other gases such as sulphur dioxide and carbon monoxide are all emitted from a volcano, often with explosive force. As the steam rises into cooler layers of the atmosphere, it condenses and torrential rain adds to the general chaos of the eruption.

Among the solid or *pyroclastic* materials there is always a vast amount of very fine dust. So fine and light is this volcanic dust that it takes months, even years, to float down out of the atmosphere. On the beds of the great oceans there are layers of fine red clay, the accumulation of dust from distant volcanoes. The dust which comes down on the land soon gets mixed with the soil, but in the centres of ocean beds there is very little else. In 1883 occurred what was probably the biggest natural explosion in recorded history. The island of Krakatoa near Java was suddenly blown to pieces, and the explosion sent into the air dust which is thought to have drifted all round the world, and to have caused wonderful sunsets in places as far away as Britain a year later.

Minor Forms of Eruption. Not all volcanic activity is as terrifying as the Krakatoa or St. Pierre explosions. In the North

Aerofilms

FIG. 32—'Old Faithful' Geyser in Yellowstone National Park, U.S.A.

Island of New Zealand there is a thermal area in which several interesting—and amusing—things can be seen. There is, for instance, Lake Taupo, the water of which is quite warm; a hole in the ground out of which large pieces of rock are continually being thrown; and even two streams running side by side, in one of which the water is cold and in the other almost boiling. You can catch a fish in the cold stream and cook it in the hot one without taking it off your line!

In the Yellowstone National Park in the U.S.A. a similar thermal area contains a large number of *hot springs* and *geysers*. The Mammoth Hot Springs pour scalding hot water down a series of steps which they have themselves built up from the calcium carbonate dissolved in the water. One of the geysers in the Park throws up a column of hot water and steam at such regular intervals that it has been given the name of 'Old Faithful' (Fig. 32). Underground water is heated and turned to steam below the surface to the point at which sufficient pressure has been built up to cause an explosion.

Volcanoes Dormant and Extinct. Some volcanoes have not erupted for so long that we may safely assume them to be extinct or dead, but with others we are not quite so sure, and they are therefore described as dormant or 'sleeping' (Fig. 33). Throughout the world countless hills or sheets of lava represent the remains of extinct volcanoes many millions of years old. On a geological map these are nearly always coloured red. In some places the ancient lavas did not actually reach the surface but managed to force their way between layers of sedimentary rocks and often caused the surface rocks to bulge above them. A sheet-like intrusion of uniform thickness is called a *sill*, while a dome-shaped intrusion is known as a *laccolith*. A *dyke* or intrusion running across the strata may be formed of the solidified contents of either the pipe feeding a sill or laccolith or, on a larger scale, the pipe which led upwards to the mouth of

Ewing Galloway, N.Y.

FIG. 33—Mount Lassen in California. Although this is now considered an inactive volcano, it erupted in 1914 and 1915.

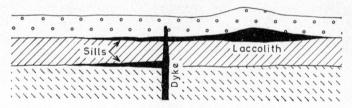

F<small>IG</small>. 34—Types of igneous intrusion.

a volcano (Fig. 34). In the Le Puy district of the Central Plateau of France several plugs of extinct volcanoes, from which the surrounding cones have been worn away, stand out like gigantic monuments, in some cases crowned by churches.

EARTHQUAKES

In an earthquake waves are formed in the earth's crust just like the ripples which form in a pond when a stone is thrown into the water. If you were so unfortunate as to be close to the centre of a big earthquake, you would actually feel the ground hitting the soles of your feet like a hammer as the waves passed beneath you.

Distribution of Earthquakes. Earthquakes are particularly frequent along the lines of weakness in the crust where are found the young fold mountains and the big fault lines. It is thought that earthquakes are caused when the two sides of a fault slip against each other. The central point or *focus* from which the waves start often lies about 20 or 30 miles below the ground, and from this point the various types of wave are sent outwards. Delicate instruments known as seismographs can detect waves from an earthquake on the other side of the earth, and geologists in charge of them can tell by the nature of the marks made on the recording sheet not only that an earthquake has taken place, but also how big it was and roughly how far away was the *epicentre* or point on the earth's surface immediately above the focus (Fig. 35). It is by studying the wavy lines made on the recording sheets that we have also discovered a great deal about the crust of the earth and the nature of the rocks that lie beneath (Fig. 36).

The Effects of Earthquakes. Earthquakes in England are fortunately rare. Several have occurred in the last 25 years, but they were only slight, and people in the affected areas either thought that a heavy lorry had passed the house or quite failed to notice them. But in Japan hundreds occur every year. By far the greater number of them are so insignificant that no one shows

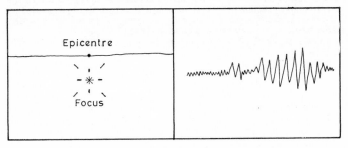

Fig. 35—The epicentre and focus of an earthquake.

Fig. 36—Part of the recording made by a seismograph during an earthquake.

much concern. If an earthquake is rather more severe, the occupants of a room may go and stand in the doorway, so as to lessen the risk to themselves if the walls fall down. But every ten years or so there is usually a really big earthquake, and tremendous damage is done. In countries like Japan most of the large or important buildings are made on a frame of steel girders and constructed specially to withstand shaking. In spite of such precautions as these, it is often impossible to prevent considerable devastation and loss of life, caused more by the after-effects of the earthquake than by the earthquake itself. One of these is fire, and the other is flooding. Earthquakes sometimes produce vast tidal waves or *tsunamis*, which come flooding in over the disorganised towns and villages.*

'During the great earthquake which destroyed Port Royal in Jamaica on June 7, 1692, the immense waves submerged 2,500 houses in three minutes. The waters remained 33 feet above the highest buildings in the town. The large English frigate, the *Swan*, was carried safely over the town and later escaped to sea!'†

* The earthquake which occurred near Concepcion in Chile on May 21–23, 1960 was one of the most violent on record. Widespread damage was caused, largely owing to disturbance of the waters of the southern Pacific Ocean, but loss of life was less than might have been expected. In an earthquake in China in 1556 as many as 830,000 people are estimated to have been killed. In Great Britain only one person is known to have died as the result of an earthquake (a child, in 1884).

† Frank W. Lane, *The Elements Rage* (Country Life, Ltd., rev. ed. 1948), p. 141.

CHAPTER FOUR

Earth Sculpture

DENUDATION

QUITE apart from the more spectacular events described in the previous chapter, the earth's surface is continually being re-moulded and modified by slow and almost imperceptible processes. Every stream and every wave plays its part in rearranging the materials of the crust and reshaping the scenery. So constant and so effective are these processes that they can in the course of time wear down lofty fold mountains to a *peneplain*—a large, almost flat area of old, hard rocks, only very slightly above sea-level (Fig. 37).

Sea-level

FIG. 37—Stages in the formation of a peneplain.

Nature uses various tools to remodel the features of the earth's surface, but the chief one is running water. Rain falls from the clouds and a multitude of tiny streams and rivulets join to form rivers, which eventually find their way down to the sea. The surface waters of the sea, heated by the sun, evaporate, and in the form of invisible water vapour are taken up into the air again. As the water vapour rises into higher and colder parts of the atmosphere, it condenses into droplets of water, to become cloud once more (Fig. 38).

Since the links in the above chain of processes are never broken, a continuous supply of water falls upon the earth. As this water travels downwards to the sea, it wears away particles

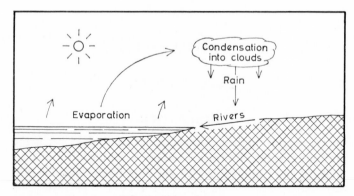

Fig. 38—The water cycle.

from the rocks over which it flows, carries them along with it, and eventually lays them down near the coast or actually in the sea. The waters of the sea also are perpetually in motion owing to tides and currents, so they too help in the work of destruction and reconstruction.

When we are thinking in general terms of the wearing down of the landscape, we use the word *denudation*. But sometimes we are thinking more particularly of certain other ways in which Nature breaks up the rocks she has created. In this case we use the word *weathering*, since these processes have to do with the weather. Anyone who has had to call in the plumber to mend a burst pipe in winter knows that water expands when it freezes. Similarly in Nature the water which collects in the tiny cracks found in nearly all kinds of rocks freezes and expands in cold weather. The force exerted by the ice is so great that the rock may be split apart. Mere changes in temperature tend to do very much the same thing, for rocks are made up of a collection of mineral substances, and each of these expands and contracts at a different rate. Repeated changes of temperature therefore set up stresses in the rocks which cause them to split and crumble. This is the chief way in which the rocks are broken up in the great deserts of the world. In the Sahara Desert, for instance, although it is very hot during the day, it is often bitterly cold at night. Alternate wetting and drying of a rock also helps to break it up, and sometimes the rain-water dissolves some of the rock over which it passes, and carries this away in solution.

THE WORK OF RIVERS

Erosion. The process by which running water wears away rock is called erosion (from a Latin word which means 'to gnaw'). It may seem rather surprising that water can wear away anything so hard as rock. But if you look at a piece of stone on which water has been dripping for years, as under an old village pump, you will see a hollow in the stone worn away by the water. You can see the same sort of thing happening at the side of a stream, where the bank is being worn away. Actually, in the case of the stream, the water is probably also throwing against the bank fragments of broken rock which it has picked up earlier on. So the process is more rapid. When the water is, as it were, 'armed' with pieces of broken rock like this, we should really speak of *corrasion* rather than erosion. If the stream is flowing at all fast, it will also be rolling the stones along its bed, or picking them up and throwing them against each other, so that the corners get rounded off. This is why the stones you find in a stream are nearly always rounded and smooth.

Transportation and Deposition. Besides erosion two other important processes go on in any stream or river—namely, transportation and deposition. Moving water is capable of holding in suspension and carrying along the particles which it has succeeded in breaking off its bed and its banks or the large stones over which it has passed. The weight of eroded material it can carry along (or *transport*) depends both on its volume and on the speed with which the water is flowing. The ability of the stream to erode and transport increases enormously as its speed rises. A tiny brook moving at 2 miles per hour is sixteen times as powerful if its speed is increased to 8 miles per hour.

A startling and tragic demonstration of this was provided by
the Lynmouth disaster of 1952. A period of exceptionally heavy
rainfall turned tiny brooks into raging torrents which caused
immense destruction. A fortnight later, when the waters had
subsided, innocent little streams could be seen trickling slowly
along, while 20 or 30 feet away from their banks houses had
been torn in half, trees uprooted and great boulders swept aside
in the flood.

If the water of the stream slows down or becomes overloaded,
it has to let fall (or *deposit*) some of the material it has previously been able to hold in suspension. This is called deposition.

The River Profile. Fig. 39 shows a river profile—a section
through the length of a river from its source to the sea. The
gradient is steep in the upper part (the *torrent stage*), moderate
in the middle part (the *valley stage*), and very slight in the last
part of its course before it reaches the sea (the *plain stage*).
Nearly all rivers have a profile in three stages like this, but
there are some exceptions, caused, for example, by an outcrop
of hard rock.

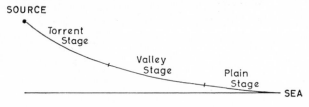

FIG. 39—A typical river profile.

In the torrent stage (Fig. 40) the river erodes downward
with considerable power, mainly by tossing about the stones
which litter its bed. The banks are usually steep and high, and a
section drawn across the channel shows a very pronounced
V-shape (Fig. 41).

In the valley stage the main river is joined by various others;
it is therefore wider, and although the gradient here is probably less than 10 feet in a mile, the current flows more rapidly.
This is due to the fact that a smaller proportion of the stream's

FIG. 40—The head of a mountain torrent in Scotland.

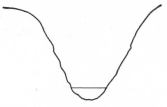

energy is expended on over-coming friction with the bed and banks. Lateral erosion is now more important than ver-tical erosion, on the insides of bends deposition has begun, and the V is very much opened out and rounded off (Fig. 42).

FIG. 41—Section across the valley of a river in the torrent stage.

In the third or plain stage the river is descending a gradient of only a few inches in a mile, and downward erosion has ceased (Fig. 43). By the time it has reached the sea, the river will,

FIG. 42—Section across the valley of a river in the valley stage.

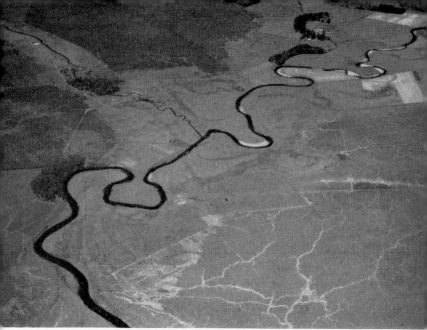

FIG. 43—The River Add in Argyll, Scotland, just before it enters the sea.
Notice the deposition on the insides of the bends.

in fact, have let fall all but the very finest and lightest particles
of eroded material and piled them up on its bed. The V is now
very much flattened (Fig. 44).

If all the above processes are allowed by Nature to go on for
a sufficiently long time without interruption in the form of some
earth-movement, it is clear that the profile of the river will
gradually change. As more and more material is removed by
erosion from the land near the upper part of the river, so the

FIG. 44—Section across the valley of a river in the plain stage.

height of the source above sea-level is progressively reduced
(Fig. 45). Various other rivers in the vicinity and countless
smaller streams flowing into them all help to wear away the

high land and build up the low land. In this way denudation is overtaking all the hills and mountains in the world, even the Alps, the Himalayas and the Andes.

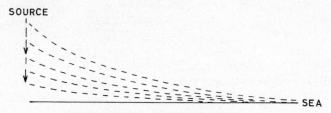

FIG. 45—The flattening and lowering of the river profile.

THE WORK OF THE SEA

While the work of denudation and deposition is going on over the surface of the land masses, the sea is continually eroding and reshaping the coastline (Fig. 46).

The movement of water at greater depths in the seas and oceans is comparatively slow, and eroded material soon sinks to the bottom, but the surface waters are often moving rapidly and can be very destructive. Fig. 47 shows the typical features of many places along our coasts. Erosion is taking place principally around the high-tide mark. The waves have been battering the cliffs for so long that they have undercut them and caused the overhanging rocks to fall as large boulders. There may even be caves, where the incoming waters have hurled themselves against weak points in the cliffs and eroded more rapidly than elsewhere. Boulders only recently fallen from the cliffs are rough and have sharp corners, while the others have been smoothed and rounded by the action of the sea.

In time these boulders are broken up, and the fragments find their way down the sloping shore to help build up the beds of stones and pebbles which we call shingle. The pebbles are rolled over and tossed about by the waves until they in turn are split, smoothed and rounded, and swept down the slope to form the

Fig. 46—Cape Cornwall near Land's End.

sand. Below the level of low tide the grains are so reduced in size as to provide little more than a layer of mud.

The sea may also transport sand and shingle along the coast.

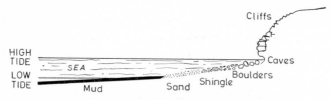

Fig. 47—Typical shoreline features.

To check this, groynes made from heavy pieces of timber such as old railway sleepers are often erected on many of our beaches (Fig. 48).

THE WORK OF ICE

The influence of weathering and running water in producing the outlines of the scenery of such places as the British Isles is reasonably obvious. Numerous features, however, cannot be explained by reference to either of the above agencies. There are valleys with sides far too steep and bottoms far too flat to

←——— TRANSPORTATION

Fig. 48—Groynes.

have been formed by water erosion, sharp ridges, huge boulders weighing hundreds of tons precariously perched in situations which suggest that they could only have been placed there by some giant, and extensive areas of clay and angular stones masking the solid rocks beneath.

Comparison with other parts of the world, where features of this kind are clearly due to present-day glaciers and ice-sheets, suggested to geologists that at some time in the past similar conditions must have existed in Britain. Subsequent research has shown that this was indeed so, and that at the height of the *Quaternary Ice Age** almost the whole of the British Isles was covered by ice, which in some places must have reached a thickness of a mile or more.

How Ice 'Flows'. It is difficult to think of ice as anything but solid, but it does in fact 'flow'. If you were to take a set of

* So called because it occurred in the *Quaternary* era of geological history. It is thought that there were at least three previous occasions when the ice-caps covering the Poles grew larger (the first one as far back as the Cambrian period), and it seems fairly certain that glacial conditions will return. But what causes 'ice-ages' has not yet been discovered.

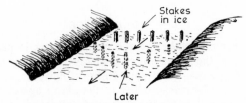

Fig. 49—Glacier ice 'flowing' down a valley.

cricket stumps to Switzerland and drive them into the ice from one side of the *glacier* (or 'river of ice'*) to the other, you would find in a few days' time that they had moved a yard or two down the valley, thus proving that the ice had 'flowed' for that distance. The stumps in midstream would have moved farthest because the ice at the edges is held back by friction with the sides of the valley (Fig. 49).

An interesting experiment can be carried out in a refrigeration chamber. If a block of ice is suspended from the ceiling by loops of wire, it will gradually lower itself to the ground. The wires will actually pass through the ice, leaving only lines of air-bubbles to mark their passage, and the block will remain unbroken (Fig. 50). As the wires sink into the block, the ice 'flows' in again behind them and closes the gap. The exact mechanism of this process is not really understood. Some

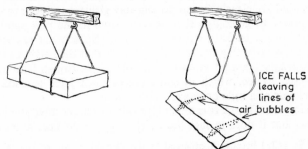

Fig. 50—A laboratory experiment to prove that ice 'flows'.

* *Not* a frozen river.

scientists think that the pressure of the wire causes the ice in front of it to melt, and that the water slips round the wire and refreezes behind it.* This is called *regelation*. Others think that the crystals of which ice is composed slide over one another, just as if you had a soup plate full of marbles or lead shot and ran your finger through them. But whatever may be the exact mechanism of the process, ice does, in its own peculiar way, 'flow'.

Glacial Erosion, Transportation and Deposition. Although ice flows so much more slowly than water, it erodes much more powerfully, particularly downwards. Valleys which were occu-

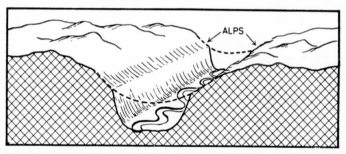

FIG. 51—A typical U-shaped valley. Benches called *alps* are often found surmounting the steep walls of a glacial valley. These represent the upper slopes of the original V-shaped valley (shown by pecked lines) which were not occupied by the glacier.

pied by glaciers during the Ice Age have a U-shaped section as distinct from the V-shaped section of water erosion. In Scotland, North Wales and the English Lake District numerous examples can be seen of valleys with steep sides and wide, flat floors carved out by the ice of long ago (Fig. 51).

The glaciers were obviously quite capable of transporting much larger and heavier pieces of rock than rivers. As they moved down the valleys, the glaciers carried along with them fragments of shattered rock which they deposited when the ice melted.

* In ice-skating the pressure of the blades momentarily melts the ice beneath them, and so 'lubricates' the surface.

THE WORK OF THE WIND

Wind Abrasion. The wind by itself is not able to erode, but just as running water uses particles of rock in the process of corrasion, so the wind may 'arm' itself with grains of sand. It is then capable of wearing away anything with which it comes in contact by abrasion.

If on a windy day you have ever been walking over an area of dry sand on the seashore, you will undoubtedly remember how keenly the grains of sand can sting as they are driven by the wind against your hands and face. In deserts like the Sahara cars which are caught in sandstorms have their paint removed and their windows turned into frosted glass. Buildings on the edges of deserts are etched and polished by the sandblast and the bottoms of telegraph poles have to be protected by piles of stones on the windward side.

The abrasive property of sand carried along in a stream of air can be put to various useful purposes. The faces of the stone used in making monuments are often polished by grains of sand forcibly directed against the stone by a jet of compressed air, and the sparking-plugs of cars can be cleaned at the garage by a machine which uses a sandblast to remove the carbon.

In regions where rainfall is very low and where weathering has broken down much of the rock into loose fragments, the effects of wind abrasion are especially noticeable. Any large rocks which may happen to stand above the level of the sand are gradually worn away on the side facing the prevailing wind, particularly near the ground where the wind is carrying its greatest load. Cliffs suffer in much the same way as solitary boulders. Their faces are undercut and caves may be formed where the sand-laden wind drives into the joints or softer parts of the rocks.

Wind Deflation and Deposition. The transportation by the wind of fragments of weathered rock involves deflation, the removal of the top layers of the surface of the land. The smaller and lighter grains are more easily picked up than the larger and

heavier ones, so that a certain amount of sorting of the fragments goes on, and clearly the lighter grains are carried greater
distances. The wind, when it meets an obstacle, lays down the
grains of sand which it has been transporting, often in heaps
called sand-dunes.

Many examples of sand-dunes can be seen around the shores
of Britain where winds from the sea have picked up the sand
and carried it a short distance inland, but none of them is so
large or so impressive as the long lines of dunes along the coast
of the Netherlands and Belgium, or, on a much grander scale,
the vast areas of sandy desert in North Africa.

Attrition. Just as the carpenter's files and chisels become
worn and blunted with constant use, so the grains of transported sand become worn and rounded by contact with ob-
structions and each other. This is known as attrition. Grains
worn down in the process of wind attrition are sometimes called
'millet seed' and are far more completely rounded than particles worn down in water.

CHAPTER FIVE

Water in the Rocks

So many houses nowadays are equipped with modern plumbing that we take it all too much for granted that when we turn on the tap an unlimited supply of pure water will issue forth. Only when a drought occurs and restrictions are placed upon the use of hoses for watering the garden or cleaning the car do we begin to think about where the water comes from or how it gets to our houses. If we happen to live in some old cottage in the country and have to fetch the water from a pump or a well, we shall certainly have given the matter rather more thought than the city-dweller.

Less than half of the water which falls as rain finds its way down to the sea. Some is evaporated by the heat of the sun and goes back into the atmosphere in the form of invisible water vapour. In temperate regions like the British Isles it is not uncommon for 60 per cent. of the rainfall to be drawn up into the air again, and in hot countries one can sometimes see rain actually being evaporated before it reaches the ground. The rest of the water which falls sinks down through the soil and into the rocks beneath.

Permeability. Rocks may be classified into the *permeable* ones, which will allow the downward passage of water, and the *impermeable* ones, which will not allow any appreciable passage. Permeable rocks owe this quality either to their *porosity* (that is, their open texture and coarse grains), such as sandstone, gravel and oolitic limestone, or to their being *pervious*, that is, traversed by joints and fissures through which water can pass, such as carboniferous limestone and jointed granite. Impermeable rocks include shale, slate and gabbro. Some rocks, however, which are porous are also impermeable, notably clay. Clay consists of extremely fine particles, separated by minute pore-spaces, but when the clay is wet ('puddled') the pores are filled with water held by surface tension, so sealing the rock against any downward passage of water.

Wells. If you were to dig down far enough into the ground, you would eventually come upon rocks which permanently contained water. If you were then to dig a little farther, you would find after a day or two that water filled the hole to the level of these saturated rocks. You would, in fact, have sunk a well. The rock formation which makes this possible is shown in Fig. 52.

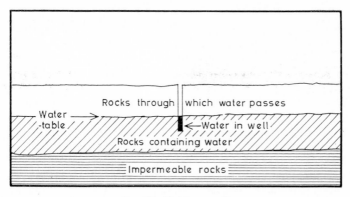

Fig. 52—Sinking a well.

The Water-table. The dividing line between the upper rocks without water and the lower rocks containing water is called the water-table. You would be able to draw water from the well as long as there was sufficient water in the surrounding rocks to keep on refilling it; in other words, as long as the water-table was higher than the bottom of the well. If, however, a long period occurred without rain, the water-table would fall, and if it fell below the level of the bottom of the well, the well would 'run dry'. If there was a long rainy spell, the water would trickle through the upper layers, and a few weeks later the water-table would rise; the well would then contain water again.

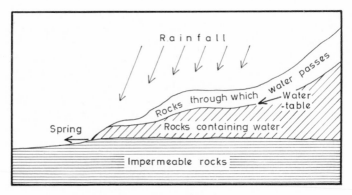

FIG. 53—The formation of a spring.

Springs. Various other arrangements of permeable and impermeable rocks may make it unnecessary for the water to be drawn out of a well. It may flow from a hole in the ground of its own accord in a spring. One such arrangement is shown in Fig. 53. You will notice that the water-table is not level like the surface of a lake, but more or less reflects the contours of the land.

Spring-line Villages. In the south-eastern parts of England where beds of chalk lie upon beds of clay, it is common to find a line of springs emerging near the base of the long, low hills which are typical of this kind of country. Early settlers found it very convenient to build their homes close to such springs. The clay rocks of the valley provided them with well-watered soils on which they could graze their cattle and grow their crops, the drier chalk of the hillside afforded pasture-land for their sheep, and a plentiful supply of clear water flowed from the springs. If you study the One-Inch Ordnance Survey maps of Kent and Sussex, you will find numerous examples of spring-line villages (Fig. 54).

Artesian Basins. In an artesian basin the water may spurt out of the well like a fountain. This occurs when 'saucers' of permeable and impermeable rocks are almost completely sealed

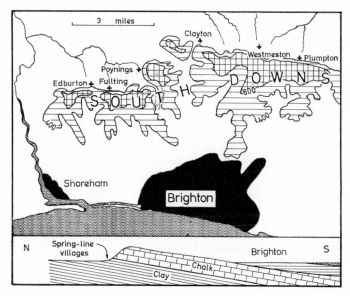

FIG. 54—Spring-line villages in Sussex.

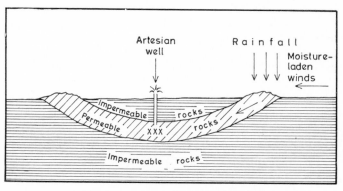

FIG. 55—The formation of an artesian basin.

over by another impermeable layer (Fig. 55). The rain sinks
into the permeable rocks where they appear on the surface or
outcrop and makes its way downwards towards the centre of
the saucer. Since it is hemmed in by impermeable rocks above
and below, the water at X in the diagram is under considerable
pressure. If, therefore, the top layer of rocks is punctured by a
well, the water will shoot up like a fountain. When a large
number of wells has been sunk in the basin, the pressure is
reduced, and it may be necessary for the water to be pumped
up. London is situated on an artesian basin, and at one time
the water rose to the top of the wells of its own accord, but so
much of it has now been drawn out that this no longer happens
(Fig. 56).

Artesian basins are very useful in parts of the world where
rainfall is low, but they often have only limited value for irri-
gating the land. The water has so many chemical substances
dissolved in it that it makes the soil 'salty' and unsuitable for
growing crops. In the Great Artesian Basin of Queensland in
Australia the water is, however, widely used for watering cattle.

Water in the Home. The water which comes out of our household taps has passed through and over many different kinds of
rocks and has absorbed many different mineral substances.
Before the Water Board for our district passes on to us the
water it has pumped up from wells or has collected in reservoirs, this water is filtered to remove any impurities or injurious
chemicals. The filtering and cleaning of the water is most
important, since it is one of the ways in which we can guard
against the spread of diseases like typhoid fever. Many of the

Fig. 56—The London artesian basin.

'plagues' of former times were due to the drinking of polluted water.

Even so, the water in one part of the country differs from the water in another part. You may yourself have thought that the water you drank on holiday last year tasted rather different from the water you drink at home. This was due to the presence of traces of various minerals. In some parts of Britain, at Buxton, Harrogate and Droitwich, for instance, the minerals in the water from some of the wells in the district are considered very beneficial, and people afflicted by rheumatism or other complaints go specially to these watering-places or spas to 'take the waters'.

One particular characteristic of some water, which you cannot fail to notice if you live in areas like Derbyshire, is its 'hardness'. Hard water contains calcium carbonate derived from the limestone over which it has passed. Calcium carbonate in the water is not in general injurious; it is, however, highly inconvenient. It prevents soap from lathering properly, and many people in hard-water districts have a 'water-softener' fitted into the intake pipe. Housewives in such areas, who at one time had to do the best they could with soap for the family washing, find modern 'detergents' very useful, since they are not affected by the calcium carbonate.

Karst Scenery. In upland areas where the surface rocks are almost entirely composed of carboniferous limestone a number of very remarkable features are found, which make up a type of scenery known as karst, a name derived from the Karst district of Jugoslavia. They are all due to the fact that limestone is capable of being dissolved by rain-water.

Carboniferous limestone contains systems of joints which divide the rock into enormous blocks. Water makes its way into these minute cracks, and trickles downwards, gradually enlarging them by solution. In time so much of the rock is dissolved that a vast and complicated network of caverns is produced, the exploration of which provides interest, thrills and sometimes tragedy for 'speleologists'.

Surface drainage in karst districts is almost negligible, but below ground, particularly after heavy rain, numerous pools and streams, sometimes of considerable size, carry the water downwards until it emerges where the bottom layers of limestone outcrop on the side of a valley (Fig. 57). Visitors to the Cheddar Caves in Somerset will recollect how attractive such underground streams can be made to appear when illuminated. Sometimes so much of the rock is carried away in solution that the roof collapses and a steep-sided gorge is formed.

Not quite all the dissolved limestone, however, reaches the open air. Where the lime-charged water drops from the roof of a cavern, it tends to leave behind it minute particles of crystalline limestone, which eventually form into long 'icicles' or *stalactites*. Similar formations build upwards from the point on the floor where the drops fall; these are called *stalagmites* (Fig. 58). Chemically stalactites and stalagmites are exactly the

FIG. 57—Section through an upland area of Carboniferous limestone.

Ewing Galloway, N.Y.

FIG. 58—(Top right) Carlsbad Caverns in the Guadalupe Mountains of New Mexico.

Eric Kay

FIG. 59—(Bottom right) A limestone pavement, showing clints and grikes, near Ingleborough in north-west Yorkshire.

same as the 'fur' which forms in kettles in which hard water has been used.

Karst regions are at best covered with only a thin layer of soil, in which there may grow sparse grasses; and large areas of bare rock are cut up by gullies, called in Yorkshire *grikes*, where solution has enlarged the vertical joints, so separating sharp ridges or *clints* (Fig. 59). Here and there are circular *swallow-holes* (or 'pot-holes'), funnel-shaped at the top and often opening out at the bottom into vast cavities from which tunnels and passages lead off in all directions. The water which plunges 365 feet into Gaping Ghyll near Ingleborough in Yorkshire produces the second highest waterfall in Britain.

The most extensive area of karst scenery of this kind occurs in north-western Jugoslavia. Further examples are to be found in the Causses district of southern France, and in England in north-west Yorkshire, parts of Derbyshire and the Mendip Hills.

CHAPTER SIX

Rivers

NOW that we have seen (in Chapter 4) something of the
tools which Nature uses in wearing down and remodelling the
surface of the earth, the actual features or land forms which
are the result of her handiwork must be discussed.

Since running water is by far the most effective of Nature's
tools, it is only to be expected that most of these land forms
should be associated in some way with rivers.

The River Basin. Every large river is fed by a number of
smaller rivers or tributaries. These tributaries are fed by brooks
and streams, and they in turn derive their water from tiny
rivulets which form as the rain trickles over the ground to begin
its long journey to the sea. The area of land which collects the
water which will eventually flow out through the river-mouth is
called the basin of the river. The basin is really more like a
saucer, though, of course, one part of the edge of the saucer is
not turned up, otherwise the water never would reach the sea!
(Fig. 60).

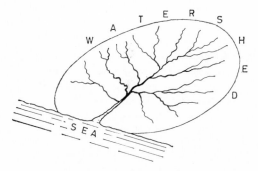

FIG. 60—The basin of a river.

The Watershed. We can divide up any large area of land into 'collecting-grounds', 'catchment-areas' or river basins. Between one river basin and the next obviously an area of higher ground divides the water draining into one river from that draining into its neighbour. The line along the top of this high ground is the watershed or *divide*. The water which falls on the roof of a shed divides in very much the same way (Fig. 61). There are, of course, minor watersheds between all the various streams and tributaries inside the river basin. It is important to remember that some land inside the basin may be higher than the watershed around it.

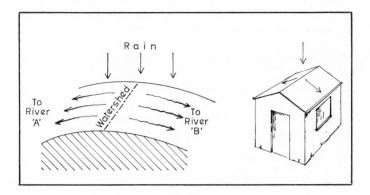

Fig. 61—The watershed.

The River Profile. As soon as each tiny rill begins to flow, erosion, too, begins. There would, however, be little point in attempting to describe in detail the effects of these early stages of erosion. We can more profitably take up the story when, after a very long period of time by everyday standards, the main river has carved out for itself a course from source to mouth which in profile looks very much like the curve shown in Fig. 39, p. 48.

The curve may not be quite as smooth and regular as would

appear from the diagram. It may be interrupted in places by waterfalls, where the stream falls over ledges of harder rock, and it may be that some kind of comparatively sudden earth-movement disturbed the river basin while the profile was being formed. The River Severn has quite a complicated profile due to the fact that three former rivers are thought to have joined to make up the present river. In many 'young' rivers, like those in the Scottish Highlands, the torrent stage occupies practically the whole of their course.

The torrent stage is sometimes described as the stage of *youth*, the valley stage as the stage of *maturity*, and the plain stage as the stage of *old age*. In one way these alternative names are helpful, since they suggest pictures of the varying character of the flow of water in the different sections of the profile, from the turbulence of youth to the stateliness of old age. But in another way they are apt to be misleading, since they tend to conceal the fact that the features of all three stages are being formed at the same time.

THE TORRENT STAGE

In the torrent stage of a river the chief work is that of erosion. The smoothing and rounding by weathering of the valley sides cannot keep pace with the downward destruction of the river bed, so that a cross-section presents a distinct V-shape. In ex-treme cases the valley is so narrow and its sides so steep that we should be justified in calling it a gorge or ravine. In mountain-ous areas such as North Wales or the Highlands of Scotland, you can find numerous examples of youthful river valleys, the water a mass of white foam as it swirls and tumbles over the boulders which litter the bed of the stream or spills over the frequent waterfalls.

Waterfalls. These are liable to occur at any stage in the course of a river where, for instance, a layer of harder rock lies across the channel (Fig. 62), but they are particularly numerous in the torrent stage. In the course of time they slowly retreat upstream, becoming lower as they go, until the profile of the

Aircraft Operating Co. of Africa, Ltd.

Fig. 62—The Victoria Falls on the River Zambesi in Africa. The Zambesi originally fell over the edge of a plateau of basalt, but the Falls have now retreated 60 miles westward to their present position, assisted by lines of weakness caused by fault lines in the basalt.

river bed is smoothed out. If under the harder rock which forms the ledge lies a layer of softer rock, the falling water undercuts the ledge by splashing back, until the overhanging rock breaks off and the process begins all over again (Fig. 63).

Hydroelectric Power. In situations where the flow of the river is sufficiently constant throughout the year, the force of the current in the torrent stage is sometimes used to drive turbines for the generation of electricity. Some generating stations are quite large, as, for instance, in the Alps or the mountains of Norway, but in Great Britain hydroelectric stations of any size are as yet confined to the Scottish Highlands (Fig. 64). Miniature plants of this kind are sometimes to be found in Wales, where the force of a hillside torrent is made to produce enough power to provide an outlying farmhouse with electric light.

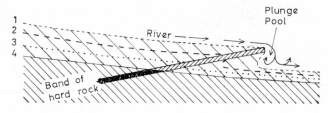

Plunge Pool
1
2
3
4
River
Band of hard rock

FIG. 63—A waterfall retreating upstream.

FIG. 64—Hydroelectric power station near Pitlochry in Scotland.

Aerofilms

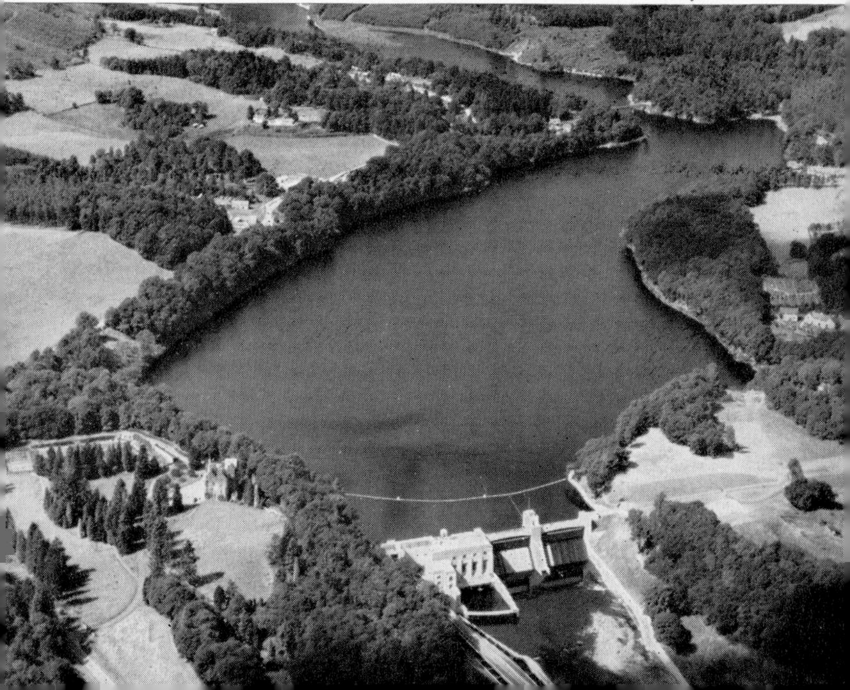

THE VALLEY STAGE

In the valley stage weathering of the banks has been able to keep pace with downward erosion of the river bed, and particles loosened and broken off by rain, frost and changes of temperature have gradually made their way down to the river and been swept away. The sides of the V representing the section across the valley have been opened out, so that the land on either side of the stream has quite a gentle slope. The relief is much smoother and more 'subdued' than in the torrent stage, and it is unlikely that neighbouring hills rise to more than a few hundred feet. If the soils are fertile, it is possible for crops to be grown, and such areas as Wensleydale (the valley of the River Ure) in Yorkshire provide excellent farming country.

Interlocking Spurs. Although erosion has not yet ceased, deposition is taking place at almost all of the numerous bends which now begin to appear (Fig. 65). The current flows faster on the outside of a bend, and at this point the bank is being

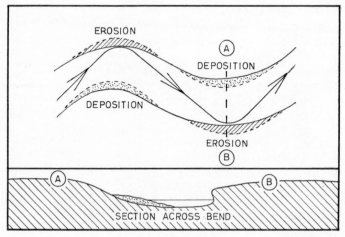

FIG. 65—Erosion and deposition at the bends of a river.

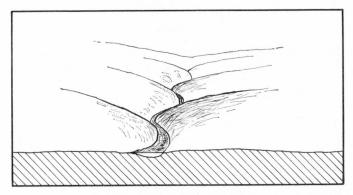

FIG. 66—Interlocking spurs.

eroded; but on the inside, where the water is moving more slowly, particles of sandy material are being deposited. Spurs of land on one side of the river interlock with those on the other (Fig. 66).

Meanders. To a very great extent downward erosion is being replaced by sideways erosion. As the current eats into the outside of each bend or meander and builds up the inside, so the course of the river becomes more tortuous. So also is each of the spurs worn into the shape of a cusp, and the general pattern of meanders moves bodily downstream (Fig. 67).

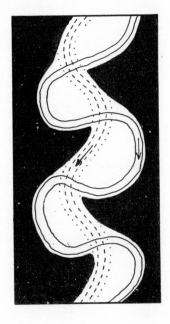

FIG. 67—Meanders becoming more tortuous and moving bodily downstream; spurs being worn into cusps.

THE PLAIN STAGE

As the valley stage passes into the plain stage, little remains of the spurs or cusps. The river winds ever more tortuously across a wide, flat area between two lines of comparatively steeply-rising ground called bluffs.

River Terraces. The greater part of the land surface between the bluffs has been built up by deposition on the insides of the perpetually shifting meanders. As the river continues to lower its bed, more recent meanders cut into the material deposited by earlier ones. Patches of gravel abandoned in this way are known as river terraces* (Fig. 68). They have provided man the world over with level sites on which to settle and fertile soils in which to cultivate his crops.

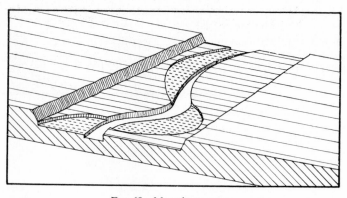

FIG. 68—Meander terraces.

In the plain stage proper the river is broad and surprisingly fast-moving, and wanders across the countryside in even wider and more tortuous meanders (Fig. 69).

The Flood Plain. If at any time more water than usual has been collected by all the various streams in the river basin, the

---

* These are *meander terraces*, and must be carefully distinguished from *rejuvenation terraces* described on p. 87.

Fig. 69—The River Thames near Staines.

level of water in the plain stage may rise above the banks, and the surrounding land will be flooded. Since this is very likely to happen, we call this area the flood plain of the river. Every time the river floods, fine particles of *silt* or *alluvium* are laid down which accumulate as a layer of fertile soil very useful to farmers in all parts of the world. In Asia the vast flood plains of rivers such as the Ganges and the Yang-tse-kiang are crowded with millions of peasant farmers growing most of the food they require for themselves and their families on 'farms' little bigger than what would in some countries be described as allotments.

Levees. As more and more material is deposited on the bed of the river, the normal level of the water rises until it is dangerously close to the top of the banks. In an effort to lessen the risk of flooding, artificial banks or levees are sometimes built, as once they were in the flood plain of the Mississippi. Actually, this increased the danger! Since the Mississippi could now deposit its load of silt only on the bed of the river itself, the level of water was again raised, and it became necessary to make the levees higher. But the river rose again—and again the levees were built higher, so that eventually the Mississippi was flowing above the level of the surrounding land (Fig. 70). However carefully the levees were watched, it was impossible to prevent small gaps from appearing. Unfortunately, on several occasions the river burst through and widespread devastation was caused to farms and buildings. Nowadays in cases like this huge dredgers are used to deepen the channel; the water is thus made to flow faster, and the silt is carried away.

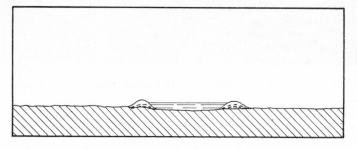

FIG. 70—Levees.

Without any interference from man, there is a tendency for rivers in flood to deposit most of the suspended material close to the river side. Banks formed in this way are called natural levees to distinguish them from the man-made levees described above.

Ox-bow Lakes. Bends in the plain stage are much more numerous and pronounced than in the valley stage. They may even cut into one another (Fig. 71). Since the banks at *A* and *B* on the outsides of the bends are continually being cut away,

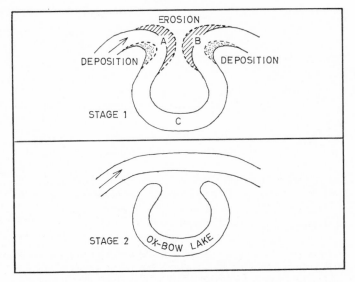

FIG. 71—The formation of an ox-bow lake.

there comes a time when *A* and *B* join up and the river by-passes
C, leaving an ox-bow lake.

As the plain stage of the river is usually navigable by shipping, the course is often straightened artificially. This not only
saves the ships time and trouble, but also helps the river to
carry away much of the eroded material it would otherwise have
dropped.

Deltas. The very finest particles of silt are transported right
down to the sea, where the flow of the river is checked and the
load is deposited on the sea bed. Normally currents and tidal
movements sweep these particles away from the mouth of the
river, but if there are no currents or if, as in the Mediterranean,
there is very little tidal movement, or if there is an unusually
large amount of silt to be disposed of, deposition may build up
a delta. This is, in effect, a seaward extension of a flood plain
(Fig. 72). The river thus tends to block up its own mouth, and

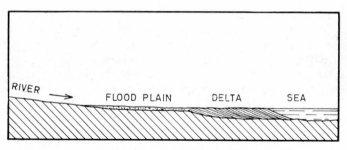

Fig. 72—The formation of a delta.

the water has great difficulty in finding its way across the obstruction. It frequently splits up before entering the sea into *distributaries*, which are very liable to change course with slight variations in the flow of the river.

Some deltas are much larger than most people imagine. The Ganges, for instance, has a delta as big as England and Wales. Deltas on a small scale, however, can often be seen where a river enters the quieter waters of a lake (Fig. 73). A more or less triangular* area of deposition fans outwards into the lake

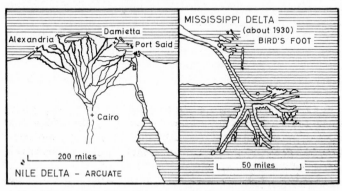

Fig. 74—The delta of the River Nile.

Fig. 75—The delta of the River Mississippi.

* The fourth letter of the Greek alphabet is Δ (called *delta*).

Swissair

Fig. 73—The delta of the River Kandar in Switzerland, where the river enters Lake Thun. Suction apparatus on one of the barges is removing the material of the delta for use as sand and gravel in the building industry.

which may in time advance so far that the entire lake is filled in. This outward growth is characteristic of deltas. The town of Adria, now fourteen miles from the mouth of the River Po in Italy, was a port in Roman times; the Rhine delta is advancing one mile in every hundred years, and the delta of the Mississippi a mile in sixteen years.

Not all deltas are shaped like what is probably the most famous one of all—the one at the mouth of the River Nile (Fig. 74), which is an *arcuate* delta. The Mississippi has a *bird's foot* delta, and it is easy to see from Fig. 75 how the name arises. Nor must it be thought that a delta is found at the mouth of every river. Usually a river becomes wider as it nears the sea until a point is reached at which the level of the water rises and falls with the tide. This wide part where the fresh water of the river mixes with the salt water of the sea is the *estuary* of the river.

DRAINAGE PATTERNS

When in the foregoing pages we traced the development of the profile of a typical river, it was assumed that the rock over which the river passed—indeed the rock of the entire basin— was of more or less the same kind throughout. The pattern of drainage resembled the trunk and branches of a tree (see Fig. 60, p. 67), and for this reason the term *dendritic* drainage is used (from the Greek word *dendron*, meaning 'a tree'). But some of the rocks over which the river and its tributaries flow may be softer and more easily eroded than others. In this case a more rectangular pattern may develop, which, since it resembles a garden trellis, is known as *trellised* drainage.

Escarpments. One very important and very common land-form which occurs in areas of trellised drainage is the escarpment or, as it is often called, the scarp. This takes the form of a long, low hill, and the essential features are a long, gentle slope on one side (the *dip slope*) and a comparatively short, steep slope (the *scarp slope*) on the other (Fig. 76). The scarp slope may be a fault scarp, caused by the slipping downward of the

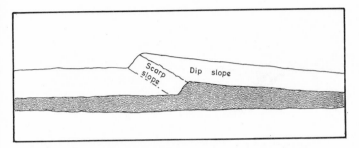

FIG. 76—The scarp slope and the dip slope of an escarpment.

land on one side of a fault line, but usually it is due to the presence of an extensive band of more resistant rock lying across the basin of a river.

Fig. 77 shows a simple anticline composed of alternate hard and soft layers of rock. Rivers known as *consequent* rivers (since they are a direct consequence of uplift) begin to flow, following the steepest slope. These are marked *C* in the diagram. In course of time denudation wears away the surface of the anticline, particularly the highest parts, and the rivers cut for themselves channels crossing the alternate bands of rock (Fig. 78). As these consequent rivers wear their channels downwards, they make water gaps in the outcrops of hard rock, and tributaries or *subsequent* rivers, flowing at right angles to the consequent rivers, carve out valleys in the softer bands of rock (*s* in

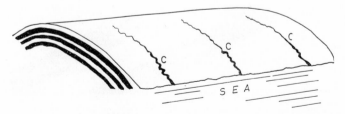

FIG. 77—A simple anticline showing the initiation of consequent rivers.

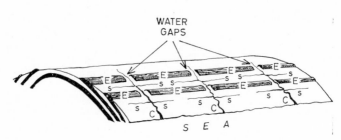

Fig. 78—The same anticline after more extensive denudation.

the diagram). The harder rocks stand out between the water gaps as escarpments (marked *E*). The dip slopes and scarp slopes are formed as a result of the tendency for subsequent streams to work their way bodily sideways down the main slope of the anticline. The stages in the process by which one side of a subsequent valley becomes steeper than the other are shown in Fig. 79.

Scarpland Scenery. Scenery in which escarpments predominate is referred to as scarpland scenery, and many examples can be seen in the south-eastern part of England (Fig. 80). Perhaps the best example of all is in the Weald of Kent and Sussex,

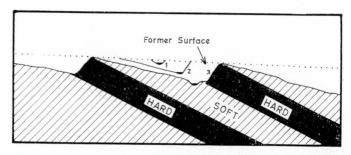

Fig. 79—The 'shifting' of a subsequent stream and the formation of the scarp slope.

FIG. 80—Part of the South Downs escarpment. Brighton is only a few miles away to the left (i.e. south) of the escarpment. Notice the spring-line villages.

which is composed of bands of rock which vary in their resistance to erosion. The area is really more of an elongated dome (or *pericline*) than a simple anticline, and the escarpments occur in pairs, facing inwards. If you travel from London to Brighton, you pass over the various escarpments on your journey—or rather you would if the railways and main roads did not make use of the gaps (Fig. 81).

There are two long and very important escarpments in England. One, made of oolitic limestone, runs from the Cleveland Hills near Middlesbrough to the Isle of Purbeck near Swanage. The other, made of chalk, extends from Flamborough Head near Bridlington to Salisbury Plain, from which three branches lead to Dover, Beachy Head near Eastbourne, and the

Rivers

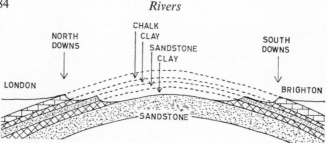

Fig. 81—Inward-facing escarpments in south-eastern England.

Isle of Wight. Various parts of these escarpments form lines of hills, the names of which are shown in Fig. 11, p. 13.

RIVER CAPTURE

All rivers and streams as they cut their channels downwards 'eat back their heads' and grow longer (Fig. 82). Under favourable conditions a subsequent river, for example, may eat back its head so far and so fast that it reaches some other river. In Fig. 83 the subsequent stream *s* has eaten back its head as far as the consequent river *C2*. If *C2* now finds that *s* provides it with a steeper slope down to the sea than it had before, it will add its waters to those of *s*, and so to those of *C1*, and will abandon

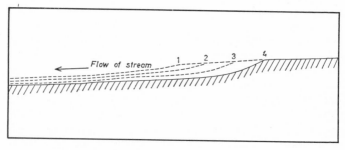

Fig. 82—A stream 'eating back its head'.

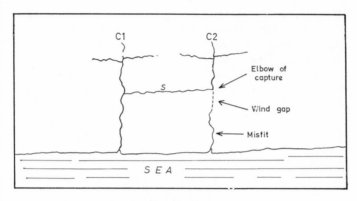

Fig. 83—River capture.

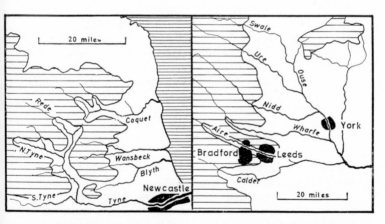

Fig. 84—River capture in Northumberland. A tributary stream flowing into the South Tyne has already captured the headwaters of the Blyth and the Wansbeck, and may in time capture the upper part of the Coquet.

Fig. 85—River capture in Yorkshire. The River Ouse 'eating back its head' along an outcrop of soft rock has captured in turn the Wharfe, Nidd, Ure and Swale. It is not possible to show the beheaded streams, as the drainage to the east of the Ouse was reversed by a later uplift of the land.

its former lower course. River capture is said to have taken place. The lower valley of the 'beheaded' river now contains a stream of water (a *misfit*) smaller than a section across the valley would suggest, and a *wind gap*—that is a valley containing no river—is left below the point of capture. The point where river capture has taken place is often revealed by a right-angled bend in the course of the stream or *elbow of capture*. Sometimes the same river may go on to make a series of captures, as may be seen from the two examples from northern England shown in Figs. 84 and 85.

<h2 style="text-align:center">REJUVENATION</h2>

We have already seen in Chapter 3 that the earth's crust is far less stable than we might suppose. It is not surprising, therefore, that some river basins have during their life-history been uplifted. In such circumstances the speed of the river's flow is increased and the channel is eroded more deeply. The drainage of the area is thus rejuvenated or 'made young' again.

The same result will, of course, ensue if the level of the sea falls. In the Ice Age, for example, vast quantities of water were locked up in ice-sheets and glaciers, and the drainage of areas not directly affected by the ice was rejuvenated.

Incised Meanders. The chief effect of rejuvenation in the upper part of a river can be seen in the particularly steep valley sides and the numerous gorges. In the middle and lower parts the river maintains its meandering course but erodes rapidly downwards at the same time, thereby producing what are known as incised (or 'cut-in') meanders. There are good examples of incised meanders in the Wye Valley in Herefordshire, and at Durham where the cathedral and castle are situated on an eminence around which flows the River Wear (Fig. 86). Probably the most impressive incised meanders of all are to be seen in the United States, where, owing to an uplift of some 7,000 feet in Tertiary times, the River Colorado, which had already reached the stage of old age, began to eat its way down-

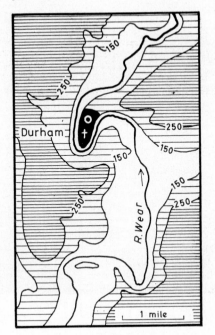

FIG. 86—Incised meanders at Durham. The city of Durham is built on an eminence surrounded on three sides by an incised meander in the River Wear. O indicates the castle and † the cathedral.

wards. In places the Grand Canyon is now well over a mile deep, and the process of down-cutting is still going on (Fig. 87).

Rejuvenation Terraces. A further effect of rejuvenation is the formation of river terraces in a manner somewhat different from that described earlier in this chapter. As the stream cuts downwards, the flood plain is abandoned and a new flood plain forms at a lower level. The portions of the original flood plain left behind between the incised meanders are called rejuvenation terraces. The same process may be repeated if further rejuvenation takes place, and by comparing the levels of the various sets of terraces we can measure the uplift on each occasion. They can usually be distinguished from meander terraces

P.G.C.S.—4

Fig. 87—The Grand Canyon in Arizona.

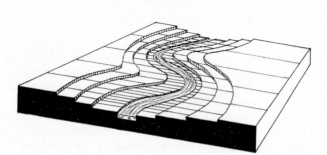

Fig. 88—Rejuvenation terraces.

(p. 74) by the way in which they occur in pairs following the general direction of the meanders (Fig. 88).

DEPRESSION OF A RIVER BASIN

The results of the depression (i.e. sinking) of a river basin are rather less spectacular than the results of uplift. The river takes on some of the features of old age. The water flows more slowly, deposition takes the place of erosion, the channel becomes choked with silt, and lagoons and marshes tend to form.

CHAPTER SEVEN

Lakes

ANY hollow in the earth's surface which remains more or less permanently full of water is known as a lake.

In Britain it is so easy to think in terms of the English Lake District and of the inland lochs of the Scottish Highlands that we fail to realise that some lakes are large enough to merit the name of seas, as, for example, the Caspian Sea, and that on lakes like Superior such violent storms take place that many a ship has been wrecked.

It is also difficult to realise that lakes may appear and disappear throughout the years. It is not often that England experiences such a dry summer as that of 1959, when many of the smaller reservoirs dried up completely. If, however, you live in Australia, you will not be at all surprised that the outline of Lake Eyre in the centre of the continent is often marked on the map by dotted lines. When that area of Australia was first explored, a lake was discovered some thirty miles wide and eighty miles long. Later visitors to the region could find nothing but a layer of salt a foot or so in thickness. Australia is a land of unreliable rainfall, and after a long dry spell the water in Lake Eyre dries up. A similar situation exists in Africa in the case of Lake Chad.

For a permanent lake to form, sufficient water must be continually added by rainfall or rivers to balance the loss by evaporation, outflow, or percolation (that is the soaking downwards of the water into the underlying rocks). Otherwise the lake will be as temporary as a puddle in the road. These 'disappearing' lakes do, however, exist where the rainfall is unreliable or unevenly distributed throughout the year.

CLASSIFICATION OF LAKES

Lakes Formed by Crustal Movements. *Tectonic* forces (that is, forces which cause movement of the earth's crust) are sometimes responsible for the hollows destined to be occupied by lakes. There are two main kinds of hollows formed by this means—those formed by sagging or down-warping and those formed by faulting.

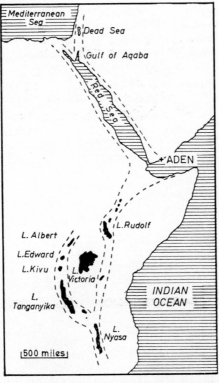

FIG. 89—The lakes of the African rift valley. The sides of the rift valley are indicated by pecked lines.

Down-warping. Lakes Eyre and Chad, and Lough Neagh in Ireland, occupy shallow saucer-like depressions where the earth's crust has sagged slightly.

Faulting. In Africa numerous examples of lakes have been caused by faulting. The deeper parts of the East African rift valley, extending northwards from Lake Nyasa to the Dead Sea, are filled with water. Lakes Nyasa, Tanganyika, Kivu, Rudolf and the others in the rift valley can easily be picked out on the map because they are so long and narrow (Fig. 89). Their floors are in many cases below sea-level. It should, however, be noted that Lake Victoria does not belong to this group; it is comparatively shallow, and was formed by crustal sagging. Another example of a lake caused (in part) by faulting is Loch Ness in northern Scotland.

The lakes of Central Sweden are due to the filling in by

FIG. 90—The Crater Lake in Oregon, U.S.A.

Ewing Galloway, N.Y.

water of the more low-lying parts of an area in which a number of faults running at right angles to each other produce a kind of 'chessboard' scenery of lakes and uplands.

Crater Lakes. The great Crater Lake in Oregon was formed by the filling with water of the crater of a vast volcano of the caldera type (Fig. 90). In various other parts of the world where volcanic activity has at some time taken place examples of such lakes can be found, from Iceland to the East Indies.

Lakes Formed by Erosion and Deposition. In many cases it is impossible to say that either of these causes is entirely responsible; a lake may be due partly to each.

Glacial erosion is particularly effective in producing suitable hollows in which lakes may form. A glance at the map of Finland or northern Canada will reveal a multitude of irregularly shaped areas of water, occupying hollows scraped out of the peneplained surface by the ice-sheets of the glacial age. The corrie lakes of Wales and northern Scotland are due to the filling of hollows, gouged out by ice near the heads of glaciers (see Figs. 95 and 96, p. 99), but deposition of morainic material probably helped in the formation of the basins.

Along the southern shores of the Baltic Sea, sand-bars (here called *nehrungs*) deposited by currents have cut off many of the indentations in the coast, so that now they form lakes known

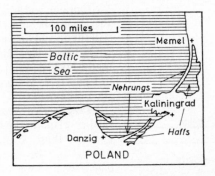

Fig. 91—Sand-bars on the Baltic coast.

locally as *haffs* (Fig. 91). The lagoons (or *étangs*) on the west coast of France south of the Gironde are due to the cutting off of indentations by the deposition of wind-blown sand (Fig. 92 and see p. 120).

Barrier Lakes. It is not difficult to visualise various natural barriers by which a valley, for instance, may be dammed to provide a hollow suitable for the formation of a lake. Many of the ribbon lakes of the English Lake District were caused by the blocking of long U-shaped valleys by heaps of material dumped by melting ice (Fig. 107, page 108). Besides morainic material and wind-blown sand, such obstacles as a landslide, a flow of lava, or even a glacier may lead to the ponding of water. Lakes formed in this way are appropriately called barrier lakes. In the long run such lakes (indeed most lakes) are only temporary features of the landscape. The dam formed by the landslide or the moraine will wear away, and the lagoon behind the sand-bar will silt up and turn into a marsh.

Ox-bow Lakes. These have already been described on p. 76 in Chapter 6, to which reference should be made.

Lakes Formed by Solution. One further class of lakes must be noticed—those caused by the sinking of the ground above places where some of the underlying rocks have been carried

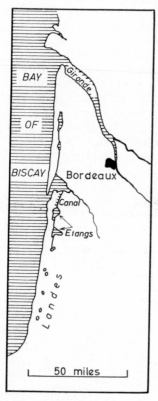

FIG. 92—Sand-bars in the Landes region of western France.

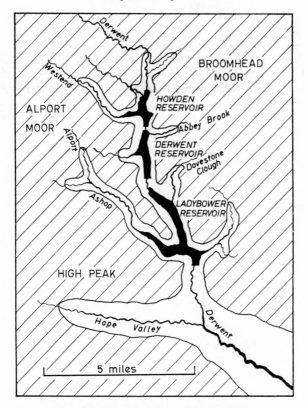

FIG. 93—Reservoirs in the southern Pennines.

away in solution. An example of this process is provided by the 'meres' of Cheshire. Beneath parts of this area are deposits of rock salt, which is soluble in water. It is thought that at any rate some of the meres are due to subsidence above places where water has percolated downwards and dissolved the salt. At Northwich some of the houses are cracking and collapsing. The sinking has almost certainly been accelerated by the

P.G.C.S.—4*

method in which the salt, which is so valuable a raw material of the Merseyside chemical industry, is 'won'. Water is pumped through the underground deposits and the brine which emerges is evaporated.

Man-made Lakes. Sometimes man in harnessing the earth's resources to serve his ends creates an artificial lake. In densely populated countries, where the supply of water for drinking and industrial purposes has to be carefully regulated and conserved, it is common for dams to be erected across a valley so that the water brought down by the river will form a reservoir. The River Derwent in Derbyshire provides a good example. Dams at three points have created reservoirs which supply the industrial areas of the Midlands (Fig. 93). More impressive examples are Lake Mead above the Hoover dam in the United States, the lake above the new Aswan dam in Egypt and the lake above the Kariba dam in southern Africa.

CHAPTER EIGHT

Ice

THE FORMATION OF ICE-SHEETS AND GLACIERS

WHENEVER you scoop up a handful of snow and squeeze it into a snowball, you are in miniature performing an operation somewhat similar to that performed by Nature in the formation of the ice-sheets responsible for moulding so much of our landscape. The loosely connected ice-crystals which make up the snowflakes are packed tightly together by the pressure of your fingers, and a certain amount of air becomes trapped in the mass. In regions of perpetual snow each succeeding fall bears down upon and compresses ever more tightly the layers beneath, until eventually there is formed a mass of *névé* (or *Firn*). This, like the snowball, is white in colour and contains a certain amount of air.

When sufficient névé has collected, it begins to spread outwards and, following the line of least resistance, flows down any convenient valley. By this time, the colour and character of the ice may well have changed. Much of the air will have been driven out, and it will have become firmer, more compact, and greenish or bluish in colour. Tongues of ice flowing down pre-existing valleys are known as glaciers, and very large areas of ice are called ice-sheets.

THE QUATERNARY ICE AGE

At the height of the Ice Age, probably 300,000 years ago, ice-sheets on this scale covered Europe as far south as a line through where Bristol, London, Utrecht and Vienna now stand. The ice fanned outwards from a centre of dispersion situated somewhere over the Baltic area, and the terms 'land' and 'sea'

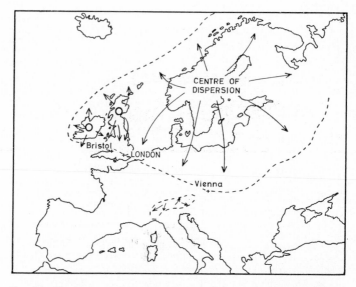

Fig. 94—The European ice-sheet at its greatest extent. There were similar ice-sheets in other parts of the world, notably in North America.

alike were meaningless (Fig. 94). The rock surface, apart from scattered *nunataks* where the topmost peaks of mountain ranges protruded above the ice, was completely invisible. Only in Greenland and Antarctica do ice-sheets now exist at all comparable with those of the Ice Age.

Now that the ice has retreated, remnants of the former ice-sheets are found as *ice-caps* in the high plateaus of places like Norway, where they are called *fjelds*.

GLACIAL EROSION

The characteristic features of land surfaces which have been subjected to erosion by the slow, relentless movement of the ice of these vast sheets can be seen, for example, in Finland or

northern Canada. The soil has been almost completely removed and the underlying rock gouged out into a multitude of
hollows like pot-holes in the road, then rubbed down and
scratched as though by a gigantic sandpaper block.

Corries. At the heads of valleys known to have been occupied
by glaciers are often found steep-sided semi-circular basins;
these are called corries.* They appear to have acted as collecting-
grounds for the ice destined to flow down the valleys as glaciers,
and probably began as shallow depressions in upland slopes
existing before glacial times. As the ice formed and flowed
away, it enlarged these hollows still further. There is still some
dispute regarding the formation of corries, but this seems to be
the most satisfactory explanation of their origin, and is to a
great extent borne out by observation in such areas as Switzerland, where the processes can be seen in operation at the
present day.

Between the walls of the corrie and the mass of snow-
covered ice within them, deep vertical cracks called *berg-
schrunds* open up, and a very intense kind of weathering known
as *nivation*, in which snow alternately thaws and re-freezes,
tears at the rock face. In this way the corrie walls become steep
and the size of the hollow increases (Figs. 95 and 96).

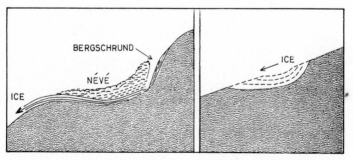

FIG. 95—The features of a corrie.   FIG. 96—Stages in the
formation of a corrie.

* Also called *cirques* or *cwms*.

FIG. 97—Arêtes near the summit of Snowdon.

Corries are very common features of glacial erosion and many excellent examples are to be seen in the Snowdon area of Wales, where they are now occupied by corrie lakes (see p. 93).

Where two corries have eaten backwards from the opposite sides of a mountain, a knife-like ridge called an *arête* may be formed (Fig. 97), such as Striding Edge, Helvellyn, in Westmorland. In Switzerland, three corries converging backwards on the famous Matterhorn have given the peak its familiar angular features and will in time destroy the upper part of the mountain completely (Fig. 98).

Glaciers and their Valleys. As soon as the ice moves over the outer lip of the corrie and begins its downward journey in the form of a glacier, the valley starts to take on a characteristic U-shaped cross-section (Fig. 99). Fragments of shattered

Fig. 98—The Matterhorn in Switzerland.

rock fall upon the surface of the glacier and sink into it. Some, their jagged edges projecting from the ice, turn the glacier into an enormous file and wear away the sides and bottom of the valley, themselves becoming further broken down in the process; others, within the body of the ice, are crushed and shattered as they are ground together in the slowly moving mass. Rock surfaces over which glaciers have passed are deeply scratched and polished by this means. It was, in fact, these scratches (or *striations*) which in the middle of the eighteenth century first gave rise to the idea that a glacial period had existed. Furthermore, the ice freezes on to the rocks which form the sides and bottom of the valley, and removes them by the process of *plucking*. The result of all these various activities by the glacier is that the floor of the valley becomes wider and flatter and the sides become steeper, so that a valley section

FIG. 99—A U-shaped valley in Norway. Notice the glacier tongue at the head of the valley.

is produced similar to those found in the English Lake District and North Wales.

Truncated Spurs. A glacier is clearly far less flexible than a body of flowing water, and in negotiating the meanders of a former river valley it will tend to blunt the interlocking spurs in an effort to carve out for itself a straighter course. Spurs blunted in this way are known as truncated spurs (Fig. 100).

Hanging Valleys. Larger bodies of ice are able to cut downwards more powerfully than smaller ones. A step was therefore formed in the Ice Age at the confluence of a tributary glacier and the larger, main stream. Where such tributary valleys are now occupied by rivers, they are called hanging valleys (Fig. 100). The confluence is usually marked by a waterfall which, since glacial times, has probably retreated some distance up the tributary stream. In the Conway Valley in North Wales are numerous waterfalls of this kind.

Roches Moutonnées. In many of the Lake District valleys, you can hardly fail to notice enormous rock-masses projecting from the ground and looking, so we are told, like the

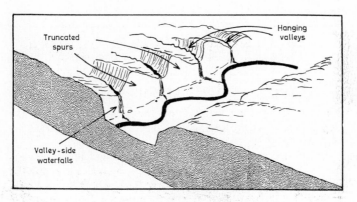

Fɪɢ. 100—Hanging valleys and truncated spurs.

moutonnées, or sheepskin wigs, once worn in France. As the ice flowed over them, it smoothed off their 'upstream' sides into a gentle incline and roughened their 'downstream' sides by plucking (Fig. 101).

Crag and Tail. This is another feature of glacial erosion, of which the classic example occurs in the centre of Edinburgh. A mass of very hard volcanic rock, which stood in the path of a glacier, protected a tapering tongue of softer rock behind it from erosion. On the hard 'crag' now stands Edinburgh Castle and on the softer 'tail' the High Street, which, together with its continuation in Canongate, forms the famous 'Royal Mile' (Fig. 102).

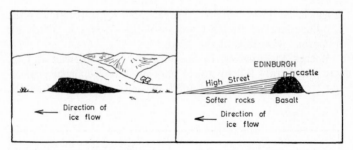

Fɪɢ. 101—A roche moutonnée   Fɪɢ. 102—Crag and tail in
                                          Edinburgh.

GLACIAL DEPOSITION

Many other striking features of the scenery are due to the
deposition of rock fragments collected and transported by
moving ice.

Erratics. Perhaps the most spectacular—and revealing—examples of transportation and deposition by moving ice are the
immense boulders called erratics, which are sometimes found
scattered haphazardly over the countryside (Fig. 103). The
materials of which the boulders are composed are often very
different from any of the rocks in the vicinity, and, apart from
moving ice, no known natural agency seems capable of having
transported them. Erratics are particularly useful in helping us
to trace the direction in which the Quaternary ice flowed.
Boulders of a rare bluish rock eroded from the tiny island of
Ailsa Craig off the west coast of Scotland are, for instance,
found in the mountains of Snowdonia. Some erratics are found
precariously poised on other rocks, in which case they may be
referred to as *perched blocks* (Fig. 104).

Moraines. Pieces of rock broken off the valley sides fall on
to the edges of a glacier as it moves along. These heaps or lines
of rock are known as *lateral* (or side) *moraines*. When two
glaciers meet, the inside lateral moraines join to form a *medial*
(or middle) *moraine* (Fig. 105). The rock fragments of moraines

Eric Kay.

FIG. 103—Erratics of Silurian grit lying on the Carboniferous limestone of the northern Pennines.

gradually sink into the ice, but whereas the lateral moraines are continually being replenished by further falls of rock, the medial moraine fades out some distance below the junction. The heap of material left behind where, at its snout, the glacier melts is known as a *terminal* (or end) *moraine* (Fig. 106).*

Terminal moraines take many different forms, but they are usually found as irregular mounds of material varying from comparatively small hummocks to lines of low hills marking the points where for the time being the ice melted. It must not be supposed that the Ice Age ended suddenly, or, indeed, that it ended gradually and evenly. Conditions appear to have grown

* It is a little misleading that the word 'moraine' should be used in the first two instances to indicate material *resting on* the ice and in the third to indicate material *deposited by* it. This is, however, the custom in geographical literature.

FIG. 105—The Aletsch glacier in Switzerland. Notice the lateral and medial moraines.

FIG. 104—A perched block type of erratic.

warmer in stages, so that many valleys are 'punctuated' by terminal moraines which mark the step-by-step retreat of the glaciers. Towards the end of the Ice Age, glaciers in the English Lake District, draining away from an ice-cap covering a dome-shaped area, carved out a pattern of U-shaped valleys like the spokes of a wheel. As the glaciers melted and retreated in stages, terminal moraines were deposited at each halting-place, and in many cases lakes have since formed between one moraine and the next. These long, narrow lakes are appropriately called *ribbon lakes* (Fig. 107, and see p. 94). Terminal moraines on a larger scale are to be found in northern Germany and Poland, where a long line of hills called the Baltic Heights rises to about 600 feet and breaks up the dull monotony of the North European Plain (Fig. 108).

Boulder-clay. Glacial deposits which are laid down in wide-spread sheets, rather than mounds or hills, are known as boulder-clay or *till*, large areas of which are to be found in eastern England and the northern parts of Europe. It consists of masses of sticky clay, embedded in which are angular stones of various shapes and sizes, and probably represents the material left behind by melting ice-sheets as distinct from glaciers. In areas where the clay is suitable for the growing of crops, the 'boulders' it contains were once a great hindrance

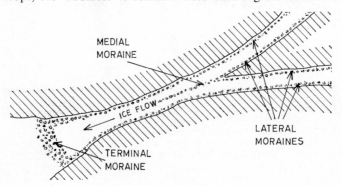

FIG. 106—Moraines.

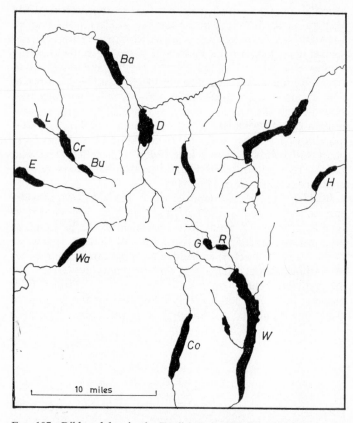

FIG. 107—Ribbon lakes in the English Lake District. Key to names of lakes. Ba Bassenthwaite, L Loweswater, Cr Crummock Water, E Ennerdale Water, Bu Buttermere, D Derwentwater, T Thirlmere, U Ullswater, H Haweswater, Wa Wastwater, G Grasmere, R Rydal Water, Co Coniston Water, W Windermere.

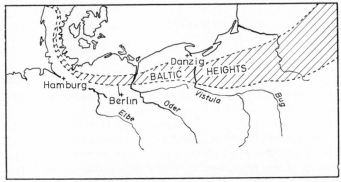

Fig. 108—The Baltic Heights. South of the Baltic Heights a number of wide, shallow valleys (called *Urstromtäler* in Germany and *Pradoliny* in Poland) run east to west. These were cut by melt-water from the Scandinavian ice-sheet.

to ploughing, but most of them have by now been removed from near the surface.

Drumlins, Kames and Eskers. In the lowlands of Northern Ireland, Scotland and northern England are found swarms of 'whale-back' hummocks of boulder-clay called drumlins, which vary from a few yards to a mile or so in length. The kames of Scotland and the eskers of Ireland are low, winding ridges of coarse sand and gravel. Although all these features are certainly of glacial origin, it is difficult to decide exactly how they were formed. Two very important points must be noticed about glacial deposits. The rock fragments of which they are composed are almost always angular and sharp, and the larger and smaller fragments are all jumbled together. Ice, unlike water, does not round off the sand and pebbles, and does not sort them out or arrange them according to size.

A certain amount of sorting and grading does, however, go on in *glacio-fluvial* deposits. These are the deposits of finer material carried away from the snout of a glacier by the melt-water. *Outwash fans* are formed in this way. If the outwash fans from two or more glaciers combine, they may make up an extensive area known as an *outwash plain*.

CHAPTER NINE

Deserts

THE word 'desert' suggests to most people a vast area of rolling sand-hills, occasional oases, blue skies and camels, and Arabs dressed in flowing garments—the sort of thing, in fact, which figures so largely in many films of romance and adventure. It is, of course, true that large areas of sand do form part of the scenery of the great deserts of the world, but a very much smaller part than is popularly imagined. It is calculated that only one fifth of the Sahara Desert, for instance, is made up of scenery of this kind.

Nor, indeed, are all deserts to be found in hot, tropical regions. The real meaning of 'desert' is 'a deserted place'—a place where no one lives, and regions near the Poles or in the centre of the Asiatic land mass are as truly deserts as the Sahara or the Atacama. Man cannot live permanently where vegetation is lacking, and no vegetation can exist where rainfall is inadequate. The word 'desert' therefore comes to mean in practice an area in which the annual rainfall is below a certain figure. How low a figure we must take to formulate a definition depends on the latitude. Rainfall which would be sufficient to support vegetation in temperate latitudes would be quite inadequate in the Tropics, where so much of it is evaporated before it can do any useful work. A round figure of 10 inches per annum is fairly satisfactory as a rough guide, but this varies with the temperature of the region, and many other factors must be taken into consideration which we need not discuss here, such as the nature of the rock and the distribution of rainfall throughout the year.

WORLD DISTRIBUTION OF DESERTS

The vegetation map (Fig. 197) on p. 223 shows where the great deserts of the world are to be found, and it will be seen that they fall into three main categories:

(i) The cold deserts or Tundra regions.

(ii) The temperate deserts, which are so far from the sea that rainfall hardly ever reaches them.

(iii) The hot deserts of the Tropics, where pressure is high in the belt of Trade Winds and rainfall comes only in occasional heavy thunder-showers (see Chapter 14).

Since the cold Tundra deserts belong in many of their aspects more appropriately to the section of this book which deals with ice-sheets, further discussion in the present chapter will be confined to the deserts of hot and temperate lands.

TYPES OF DESERT LANDSCAPE

Some geographers think that the various types of desert landscape may be regarded as stages in one long process of denudation, in very much the same way as the types of landscape formed by running water. The subject is quite an interesting one, but the details of the idea have not as yet been satisfactorily worked out. It is feasible to suppose that a landscape consisting of an unrelieved expanse of dunes, where weathering and wind action have been at work for a very long time, represents the stage of 'old age'. It is, however, more difficult to decide which types of desert landscape represent the stages of 'maturity' and 'youth'.

The problem is to some extent complicated by the fact that the climate of the desert areas may well have changed in comparatively recent times. There is good reason to believe that not so very long ago regions like the Sahara enjoyed rainfall as plentiful as that of the British Isles today. In caves in the Sahara there are little pictures scratched on the walls by prehistoric man clearly depicting his herds of cattle, and here, as

well as in other deserts, archaeologists are continually un-
earthing such evidence as the remains of cities built within
historical times. It seems likely that during the Ice Age the
climatic belts were displaced southwards, and that as the ice
retreated a gradual drying-up or *desiccation* took place of
areas that were at one time well-watered and fertile. It is,
therefore, possible that the broad outlines of much of the desert
landscape were sketched out under much wetter conditions.

Whether or not we can trace a regular sequence of events in
the development of the landscape, we can, nevertheless, distinguish four types of desert according to the features they
present:

(i) The *Hamada* type, in which the surface consists of bare,
polished rock.

(ii) The *Reg* (or *Serir*) type, consisting of vast sheets of
angular pebbles.

(iii) The mountain type, consisting of stark peaks, preci-
pitous slopes and deeply cut ravines.

(iv) The *Erg* type, consisting of extensive areas of undulating
sand-dunes.

The dominant processes which lead to the formation of all
these types of desert are weathering and wind action, but, surprisingly perhaps, water also plays a part.

WATER IN THE DESERT

Generally speaking, the less the annual rainfall is in amount
the more unreliable and spasmodic it becomes. In desert and
semi-desert areas, where the rainfall is less than 10 inches in
a year, long dry spells are broken by sudden thunderstorms.
As a result of these, vast sheets of water swill over the bare rock
surfaces, carrying along with them masses of mud, sand and
small pebbles, which they deposit as soon as the water evaporates or sinks into the ground.

Wadis. Sometimes the water carves out for itself a gorge-
like channel, called a wadi, down which it rushes so violently
that many a traveller, sheltering from the hot sun in the shade

of the steep sides, has been overtaken and drowned by a torrent of water which has originated some considerable distance away. The wadi soon becomes dry again, and the boulders and general debris which litter the floor remain until they are disturbed by the next rush of water.

Shotts and Playas. Rain (and sometimes snow) which occasionally falls upon the higher parts of the Atlas Mountains of North Africa collects in basins of inland drainage, at the centre of which are found temporary lakes called shotts. When rainfall is inadequate to maintain the lakes, the water evaporates, leaving behind a layer of salt. The *playas* or *salinas* in the Great Basin of the western United States are formed in the same way.

Oases. Although water forms so small a part of the desert landscape, it is never far below the surface. Often people have died of thirst without realising that water-saturated rocks lay only a short distance beneath their feet. Wherever the water-table comes close enough to the surface to provide moisture for the growth of vegetation an oasis will be formed. Some of the oases in the Sahara south of the Atlas Mountains are of considerable size, produce a wide variety of crops, and support a permanent population. They also provide 'jumping-off points' for journeys through the heart of the desert.

DESERT WEATHERING

The most potent agent of rock destruction in the hot deserts is weathering, and of the various forms of weathering the most effective is change of temperature. In the Sahara it is not uncommon for a midday temperature of over 100° F. to be followed by a night frost. Where the rocks are made up of a variety of minerals, these expand and contract at different rates, and a great diurnal range of temperature such as this sets up stresses which tear the rocks apart. At night-time the contraction is often accompanied by sharp sounds like pistol shots. Sudden chilling of the surface of the rocks may cause thin pieces like sea-shells to peel off in a process known as *exfoliation*.

FEATURES DUE TO WIND ABRASION AND TRANSPORTATION

The loose material formed as a result of weathering may after a thunder-shower be transported by water, but for most of the time the chief agent of transportation is the wind. The finer and lighter particles are most readily picked up, and may be carried enormous distances before they are finally dropped. The so-called 'blood rains' of southern Italy are coloured by particles of red sand originally picked up by winds over the Sahara. Other particles 'arm' the wind and enable it to abrade and polish any obstacle with which they come in contact. Horizontal areas of bare, polished rock called *desert pavements* are formed by the scouring action of grains of quartz carried along by the wind, and in some deserts the sandblast cuts into lines of weakness in the surface so as to produce a fantastic landscape of trenches and ridges running parallel with the prevailing wind. Two forms of ridges caused in this way are known as *yardangs* and *zeugen* (Fig. 109).

In the Kalahari Desert and elsewhere peculiar 'island-mountains', or *inselbergs*, rise steeply out of a sea of rock

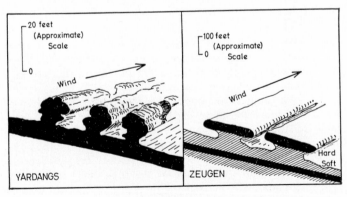

Fig. 109—Ridges formed by wind abrasion.

debris. They are invariably composed of very hard rock, and it may well be that they are 'old age' features of desert scenery which have resisted erosion (Fig. 110).

As the result of the removal of loose material, the land surface is lowered in the process of *deflation*. The *pans* of the Kalahari and larger hollows, like the Qattara Depression in Egypt, are formed in this way.

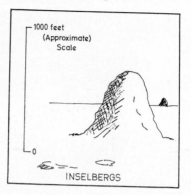

FIG. 110—Inselbergs.

When the surface of the hollow reaches the water-table, the wind is no longer able to pick up the moistened particles of rock, and erosion ceases. Many of the Saharan oases originate in the centre of such depressions.

By the time the wind has sorted over the heaps and sheets of rock debris and carried away the lighter fragments, only the heavier 'pebbles' are left behind. These are then sharpened and flattened as they lie by the action of the sandblast passing over them, until they become what are known as *dreikanter** (or *ventifacts†*).

Abrasion is most effective near the ground, where the wind is carrying its greatest load. This is well shown by isolated boulders standing above the level of their surroundings, which are often attacked at the base by the wind-driven sand, so that they become what are called *desert mushrooms*.

The above features occur mainly in deserts of the *Hamada, Reg* and mountain types (Fig. 111).

* German for 'three-sided'.
† From Latin words meaning 'made by the wind'.

Hunting Aerosurveys, Ltd.

Fig. 111—Desert near Jebel Ram in Jordan.

FEATURES DUE TO WIND DEPOSITION

The landscape of the *Erg* or sandy type of desert is much more familiar to us than the landscape of the other three types (Fig. 112). The mysterious loneliness of these vast 'seas of sand' has captured the imagination of artists, authors and even song-writers far more than the forbidding barrenness of the *Reg* and *Hamada*, but to any of us who might be condemned to cross them their 'magic' would prove far less real than the perils and hazards of the journey. They are, however, quite fascinating to study—at a distance.

The dominant process in the formation of the *Erg* is wind deposition. The particles of sand accumulate in heaps referred to as *dunes*, which occur in a variety of shapes and sizes, and are in a state of constant movement. It is fairly clear that chance

Fig. 112—Sand-dunes in Death Valley, California.

obstacles and undulations in the land surface, together with variations in the speed of the wind, set up currents and eddies which lead to the deposition of the sand in heaps or ridges, but the precise manner in which any particular pattern of dunes is built up is not as yet properly understood.

Types of Dunes. In the great deserts of the world the sand is rarely laid down in such random heaps as the dunes found in various parts of the British Isles. Sometimes the landscape displays a pattern of *barchans* (Fig. 113), shaped in plan like crescent moons, with their convex sides facing the prevailing wind and varying in size from a yard or two to hundreds of yards from tip to tip. Sometimes long ridges of sand, called *seif-dunes*, are formed, running parallel to the wind for forty or fifty miles without a break, and reaching a height of 200 feet or more. Sometimes the ridges run at right angles to the wind, and

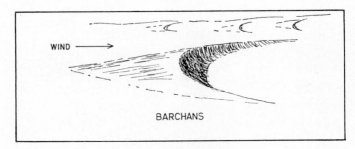

FIG. 113—Barchans.

in some areas, for no apparent reason, the sand remains as a flat surface without any undulations at all.

Dune Movement. Sand-dunes are never still, and it is possible to see something of the mechanism of their movement by watching sand grains being blown up the gently sloping face of a dune facing the wind, sliding over the top, and falling down the steeper, leeward side. The grains are gradually removed from one side of the dune to the other, and the entire formation advances downwind (Fig. 114).

One of the most mysterious features of sandy deserts is the 'vibrant, booming noises' which are occasionally heard. All sorts of fantastic explanations have been given for these noises, but they are almost certainly caused by a kind of vibration set up by sand grains tumbling over each other as they pour down a slope. Such 'roaring sands' have been reported from places as far apart as Egypt and the Atacama Desert in northern Chile.

This slow movement forward, or migration, of sand-dunes

FIG. 114—Dune movement.

FIG. 115—Sand-dunes on the shore of Ettrick Bay in the Kyles of Bute Scotland.

close to inhabited or cultivated areas, railway lines and so on, can obviously present a very serious problem, not only on the edges of the great deserts, but also along the coastline of some European countries. These are not, of course, true desert areas, but in their small way they have many features in common with the sandy regions of the Sahara. Fig. 115 shows an example of the encroachment of sand-dunes upon agricultural land.

The Culbin Sands. The most remarkable sand-dune area in the British Isles is the Culbin Sands, on the coast of Moray-shire not far from Inverness. In the last 250 years the sandhills have advanced inland, and have 'finally led to the complete obliteration of houses, farms and orchards, and even to the burial of fir plantations'.* Quite apart from total devastation

* A. Holmes, *Principles of Physical Geology* (Nelson, 1946), p. 261.

P.G.C.S.—5

such as this, sand may be swept into the air and carried inland by the wind, and may damage otherwise fertile soil. A coarse, spiky grass called *marram*, which will grow in sand, is often planted to 'fix' the dunes, and lines of trees are arranged to break the force of the wind and catch the sand.

The Landes. In the Landes region of the Aquitaine coast of France a similar situation once existed. Sand, blown inland from off the dunes which had formed along the bars built up by coastal currents, turned the indentations into lagoons and marshes (see p. 94). The inhabitants have, however, been ingenious enough not only to abate the nuisance by planting trees to fix the dunes, but to turn to their own advantage the unpromising situation. The trees now provide them with a valuable source of turpentine and pit-props for the coalmines in the north of France.

Loess. In northern China a large area is covered by a loose material called loess, formed of fine particles of yellowish dust blown from the Gobi Desert. The River Hwang Ho, which passes through the region, derives its nickname—the 'Yellow River'—from the yellow colour given to it by the dust which falls into its waters. The land surface where this dust has been deposited is very fertile, but loess is soft and easily reduced to powder, and roads are so very quickly worn down by traffic that they soon become steep-walled gorges.

In some northern parts of Germany, in the U.S.S.R., and in other areas, similar deposits are formed of fine particles ground down under the glaciers of the Ice Age and blown southwards by the winds from off the ice-sheet. These, too, are known as loess, and are very fertile. The *limon* of France and Belgium and the *brick-earth* in southern England may also have been derived in much the same way. Limon, like the loess of Germany, is particularly suitable for the growth of sugar-beet, and one use at any rate for the brick-earth can be gathered by travellers to London on the Midland Region railway line from a prominent group of tall chimneys, on which appear the words 'London Brick Company'.

CHAPTER TEN

The Sea Coast

NEARLY everyone in Britain nowadays has been to the sea-side. This is not surprising, as it is impossible to live much more than a hundred miles or so from the coast. It is, however, un-fortunate that so few holiday-makers look beyond the man-made adaptations, the sea walls, promenades and piers, to the natural features of the original coastline, since these provide such an interesting field of geographical study.

In this chapter we shall describe and classify the actual features formed by the processes outlined in Chapter 4.

A shoreline is formed whenever any part of the earth's crust comes in contact with the surface of the sea. If no move-ment took place in the body of water where it met the land, there, apart from a very small amount of chemical solution, the matter would end. As it is, however, waves, currents and tides combine to modify the line where land and water meet.

The Shore Profile. In very much the same way that we may draw a river profile, so also we may draw the profile of a typical shoreline. The stages in the development of the shore profile are shown in Fig. 116, in which it is assumed that uplift has caused the land to meet the sea in a gentle slope. The sea first cuts in the land a notch, which is by degrees extended farther and farther in depth until it becomes what is known as a *wave-cut platform*. The material acquired by erosion of the land is swept into the sea and deposited just off-shore, so that even-tually a point is reached at which a section across the shoreline displays the features shown in Fig. 116 (*e*). The first stages in the development of the profile pass quite rapidly, but the pro-cess gradually slows down, until erosion and deposition almost completely cease.

The principal agency responsible for producing this profile

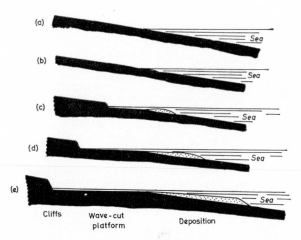

FIG. 116—Stages in the development of the shore profile.

is the action of waves breaking against the shore. Currents play only a small part at this stage, although they are important in the formation of various features to be described later, and the tides merely increase the area over which destruction takes place.

WAVES AND THEIR WORK

Wave Mechanism. In the open sea waves are essentially due to the wind, which heaps up the water in undulations. They travel in the same direction as the wind, and it is important to remember that it is the wave shape which moves forward, not the water of which the wave is composed. A cork floating in the sea moves forward on the crest of a wave and backwards in the trough to its original position, so that as each wave passes the cork describes a circular motion (Fig. 117). The height of a wave in feet (that is the vertical distance from crest to trough) is roughly half the speed of the wind in miles per hour. Only in very severe storms, therefore, do waves exceed a height of forty or fifty feet.

In shallow water friction against the bottom prevents the water in the trough from moving backwards as quickly as the water in the crest advances. Here, therefore, a floating cork does move forward a short distance every time a wave passes. When the depth of the water is less than the height of the wave, the crest falls forward as a *breaker* and forms a seething mass of surf. The final rush of water up a sloping beach is known as the *swash*, and the retreating, 'sucking' movement before the next wave breaks is called the *backwash*.

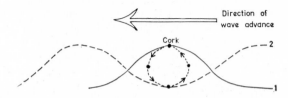

Fig. 117—Movement of a floating cork with the passing of a wave.

The Effects of Wave Action. The force of the water thrown forward in the crest of a wave is very considerable. In storms the pressure against a sheer cliff face may well be in the region of several tons per square foot. It is clear that sea walls which have to resist waves approaching over deep water must be of enormous strength and thickness. The water initially attacks lines of weakness in the rock face, such as joints and bedding planes, traps and compresses the air in gaps and fissures, and forces the rocks apart. The fragments, besides being tossed about by the waves and broken down further, are used as weapons with which to attack the land.

The onslaught is clearly most effective at the level of the crests of the advancing waves. Below this level, which will, of course, vary slightly with the tides (see p. 152), the erosive power of the water decreases with depth. A platform is thus carved in the land, and the material removed in the process of destruction is carried away seawards by the *undertow* or under-current which accompanies the slight heaping up of the water against the shoreline. As the platform becomes wider, a line of cliffs of increasing height is formed, and the off-shore area of deposition is built farther outwards.

Since the outer part of the platform has been subjected to grinding and scouring by rock fragments for the longest time, a gentle slope develops. The speed of the advancing waves is thus checked by the increasing shallowness of the water. A state of equilibrium is thus more or less reached in which cutting back of the cliff face ceases and the shoreline takes on the features described in Chapter 4 (see Fig. 47 p. 52).

The air driven into a cave by the advancing water is sometimes under such high compression that the cave is extended backwards and upwards until a *blow-hole* is formed (Fig. 118). On parts of the Cornish coast, for example, holes are found in the ground near the edges of the cliffs out of which come showers of spray from waves breaking in the caves beneath. If two caves on opposite sides of a headland run into one another, the result will be an *arch*. With further erosion the roof of the arch may collapse, leaving an isolated *stack* such as the 450 foot high Old Man of Hoy in the Orkneys. The famous Needles, which stretch in a line westwards from the Isle of Wight, are the remains of a ridge of chalk through which the sea has broken (Figs. 119 and 120).

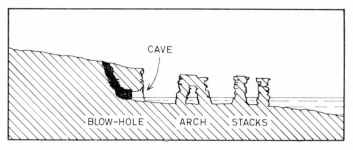

Fig. 118—Blow-hole, arch and stacks.

Fig. 119—Caves at Freshwater Bay, Isle of Wight.

Fig. 120—Chalk cliffs and stacks at Foreland Point in Dorset. Swanage can be seen in the distance.

Wave Refraction. As the waves driven by the wind at an angle to the shore advance towards a shelving coastline, friction with the bottom holds them back at *A* (Fig. 121), so that they crowd together. But the waves at *B* are able to pass freely on their way, until they too are held back, at *C*. This 'bending' of the lines of waves so that they finish parallel to the shore is known as wave refraction.

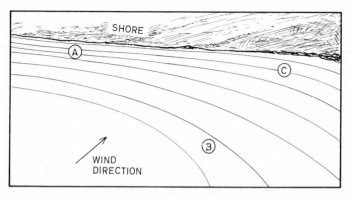

FIG. 121—Wave refraction on a straight coast.

Where the coastline is indented, wave refraction is responsible for wearing back the outstanding headlands. As shown in Fig. 122, the waves approaching from *X* turn inwards and concentrate their attack on the headlands, whereas the waves approaching from *Y* fan out and dissipate their energy in the bays. As the headlands are worn back and the bays become less deep, more erosive energy is left to be spent on the bays, so that a kind of balance is reached and the whole coastline moves landwards while keeping to more or less the same outline.

Although it is in general true that waves tend to break parallel to the shore, local circumstances often prevent their being exactly parallel. In this case eroded material is carried slightly along the shore by the swash and still farther along by

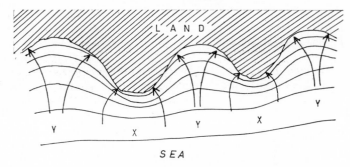

Fig. 122—Wave refraction on an indented coast.

the following backwash (Fig. 123). This gradual movement of material along the coast is called *longshore drift*, and leads to the erection of breakwaters and groynes, which are so familiar a sight at many seaside resorts. The direction of the drift, and the way it is related to the angle at which the waves break on the beach, can easily be seen from the sand and shingle heaped up on the same side of each groyne (see Fig. 48, p. 53).

The sand and shingle on the beach act as a kind of brake, and check the erosive energies of the waves. If they are removed by longshore drift, the coastline will be further eroded at this

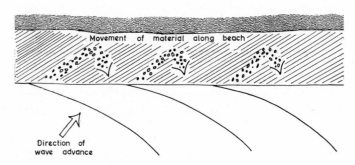

Fig. 123—Longshore drift.

point. When this happens close to an inhabited area, it presents a particularly serious problem. Parts of the coast near Eastbourne are said to have lost four or five yards a year for the last century.

No mention has been made of several other factors which affect the character of a shoreline. It would take far too long to follow up all the variations of the typical features which result from these factors, but it is obvious that a great deal will depend on the hardness and resistance of the rock, the height and steepness of the land opposed to the sea, the slope of the strata and so on. Nor is it possible to give any general figure for the rate at which the land is cut backward, but some idea of the rate at which it can take place may be gathered from the example given above, or from the following quotation:

'A picture of Reculver's church in Kent, taken in 1781, shows quite clearly 100 yards of land between the church and the sea; while another, taken in 1834, shows the church at the edge of the cliff'.*

CURRENTS AND THEIR WORK

Spits. Some of the finer material eroded from the land by waves and deposited in the shallow waters of the foreshore may be picked up by coastal currents and transported farther along the shore. It may eventually reach the mouth of a river or a bay. Here, in the deeper, quieter waters, it will be deposited, and in time, as more material is added, it will pile up until it becomes a spit or tongue of newly formed land across the bay or river mouth. Spurn Head at the mouth of the Humber has been built up in this way by material derived from the coast of Yorkshire to the north (Fig. 125. Also see Fig. 124). The rocks in the vicinity are soft and easily eroded, and a southward-flowing current has carried away so much of the eroded material that the coast has been cut back a mile since the Nor-

* W. W. Watts, *Geology for Beginners* (Macmillan, 1929), p. 64.

FIG. 124—Sand-spit at Sandbanks, near Bournemouth.

man Conquest. In 1399 Henry IV is reported to have landed at the thriving port of Ravenspur, close to where Bridlington now stands. But Ravenspur and a number of other places known to have existed in the neighbourhood have disappeared.

There are further examples of spits across the mouths of the River Yare and the River Alde in East Anglia (Figs. 126 and 127).

Bars. When a spit is so long that it reaches right across an indentation in the coastline, it is known as a bar. The most remarkable example of deposition of this kind is Chesil Bank in Dorset. A shingle bar extends for about sixteen miles along the coastline and joins the 'Isle' of Portland to the mainland. The long, narrow area of tidal water behind the bar, the Fleet, can

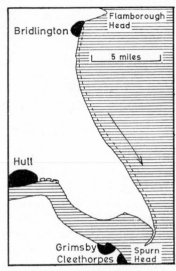

FIG. 125—Spurn Head. In this and in the following three diagrams the direction of the coastal current is shown by an arrow.

actually be entered through Portland Harbour. The bar presents the most unusual spectacle of two beaches backing on to one another (Figs. 128 and 129).

On the shores of the Baltic Sea spits and bars (*nehrungs*) have been formed, enclosing considerable areas of water (see Fig. 91, p. 93), and for about 100 miles along the Aquitaine coast of France similar bars have been built by currents across the indentations. Here, as so often happens, many of the lagoons behind the bars have silted up and have become marshes (see Fig. 92). The straightening out of coasts in this way deprives shipping of sheltered anchorages and hinders the economic development of the coastal areas.

SHORELINES OF EMERGENCE

Certain distinctive types of shoreline display features indicating that the relative levels of land and sea have altered in comparatively recent times. Shorelines formed by the uplift of the land (or, what would amount to the same thing, a fall in sea-level) are called shorelines of emergence. Shoreline features due to emergence are really quite rare, since in recent times more land has been 'drowned' than uplifted. Raised beaches (see p. 25) are found in various parts of Scotland—the northern side of the Firth of Tay and the Hebrides, for instance —lying at different heights between 10 feet and 100 feet above

FIG. 126—The spit across the mouth of the River Yare.

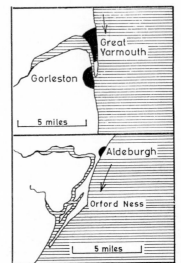

FIG. 127—Orford Ness—the spit across the mouth of the River Alde.

FIG. 128—Chesil Bank.

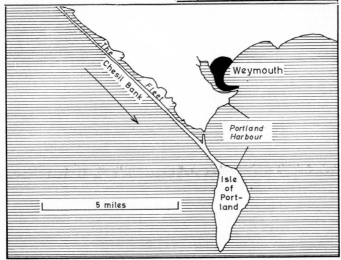

Fig. 129—Chesil Bank.

the present coastline. The Fall Line in the U.S.A., running from Philadelphia to Macon in Georgia, is thought to have once been a line of cliffs (Fig. 130). In front of it the present land surface slopes gently to the sea, now 100 miles or more away, and the rocks of which it is composed show every sign of having been laid down off some geologically recent coast.

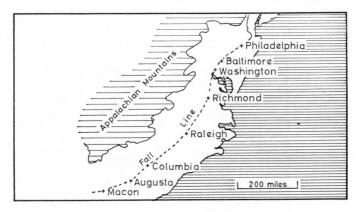

FIG. 130—The Fall Line in the U.S.A.

SHORELINES OF SUBMERGENCE

Since the end of the Ice Age, sea-level is calculated to have risen about 300 feet. It is not, therefore, surprising that 'drowned' shorelines, or shorelines of submergence, should be more common than shorelines of emergence.

In the case of *Atlantic* coastlines, where the grain of the mountains runs at right angles to the coast, a series develops of long, narrow inlets separated by equally narrow headlands. The Kerry region of south-west Ireland provides a good example of this type (Fig. 131). On a *Pacific* coastline, where the trend of the mountains is parallel to the coast, the inlets are also long and narrow, but follow the grain of the mountains, as shown by the Dalmatian coast of Jugoslavia (Fig. 132). The terms *discordant* and *concordant* are sometimes used with very much the same significance as Atlantic and Pacific respectively. The Dorset coast near Swanage displays in one small area stretches of the two kinds of coastline (Fig. 133).

Ria* Coastlines. These are found in Devon and Cornwall, the Pembroke peninsula of Wales, the extreme north-west of France, in north-western Spain, and in many other parts of the world. A glance at a large-scale map of any of the above dis-

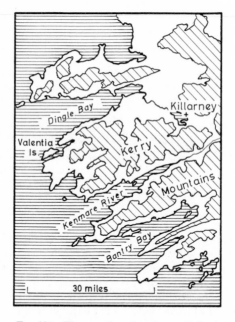

FIG. 131—The coastline of south-west Ireland. This is an Atlantic or discordant coastline, where the grain of the mountains runs at right angles to the coast.

* A Spanish word meaning 'estuary' or 'bay'.

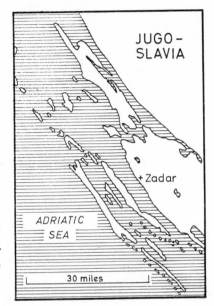

FIG. 132—The Dalmatian coastline of Jugoslavia. This is a Pacific or concordant coastline, where the grain of the mountains is parallel to the coast.

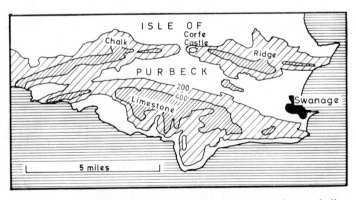

FIG. 133—The coastline of Dorset, showing both concordant and discordant stretches.

tricts is sufficient to enable one to recognise their characteristic features (Fig. 134). Rounded inlets are often grouped around a common indentation in the coastline. The streams which enter these inlets look far too insignificant to be entering such wide estuaries, and the submarine contours reveal the fact that the water in the indentation is quite shallow. Sections drawn across the inlets or rias make it easy to realise that such a coastline has

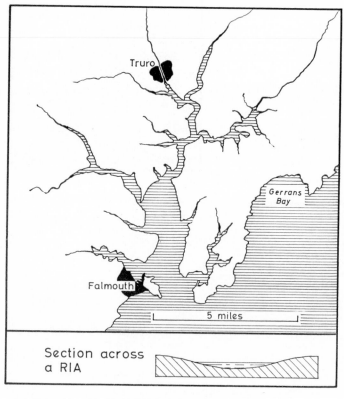

Fig. 134—Ria coastline in Cornwall.

been formed by the inundation of the lower parts of the valleys in an area of hilly country (Fig. 135).

Fjord Coastlines. These are a form of discordant coastline in which glacial erosion and submergence have played an equally important part. The coastlines of Norway, western Scotland, the southern end of the South Island of New Zealand, and various other regions in the cool temperate zones consist of numerous long, narrow inlets roughly at right angles to the coast (Figs. 136 and 137). The sides of these fjords (or sea-lochs as they are called in Scotland) are steep, and the water often reaches a depth of several thousand feet. It is, in fact, possible in many of them to get large ships quite a long way inland, and very close to the side. The fact that a section across a fjord reveals all the characteristics of a U-shaped valley has suggested the following explanation of the formation of this type of coastline.

FIG. 135—The River Yealm, near Plymouth. Notice the interlocking spurs of the 'drowned' river valley.

Aerofilms

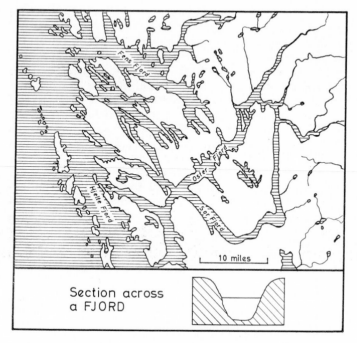

Fens Fjord

Hielle Fjord

Osier Fjord

Sör Fjord

10 miles

Section across a FJORD

Fig. 136—Fjord coastline in Norway.

It is thought that rivers which existed before the Ice Age flowed along lines of weakness caused by a series of criss-cross fault lines, running, as fault lines often do, at right angles to each other. During the Ice Age these river valleys were carved into U-shaped valleys and 'over-deepened' by glaciers which drained the vast ice-sheets on the higher ground. At the end of the Ice Age the sea-level rose, and the U-shaped valleys were 'drowned' by the water previously contained in the glaciers and ice-sheets.

Fjords have one peculiarity, which has never been satisfactorily explained—the *threshold* or ridge at the entrance to

Fig. 137—A fjord in southern Norway.

the sea, where the water is a mere 200 feet or less in depth (Fig. 138). Another strange feature of the coast of Norway is the line of low islands, called *skerries*, about twenty-five miles out to sea. These may have been formed by the deposition of morainic material in hummocks on a wave-cut platform existing from before glacial times.

It is not difficult to imagine how the early inhabitants of such regions as Norway would not only be driven by lack of flat and cultivable land to look to the sea for their food supply, but would also be tempted to undertake the crossing of a fjord by boat rather than make the long journey round it by land. The same sort of situation exists today in western Scotland, where visitors usually find it quicker to take their cars across a loch by ferry than to travel round the head of the loch by road. Familiarity with the waters of the fjords soon led to mastery of

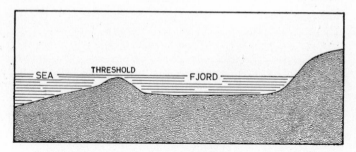

FIG. 138—Section along a fjord, showing the threshold.

the open sea, and from the coasts of Norway came the Viking*
raiders to the shores of England.

CORAL COASTS

One further type of coastline remains to be discussed—the
coral coastlines found in the warm, tropical waters of the Pacific and Indian Oceans.

Corals. There are many different kinds and sizes of these
peculiar little sea-creatures, but they all have the property of
being able to build for themselves, by taking calcium carbonate
out of the sea water, 'shells' in which they live and die upon the
dead bodies of their ancestors. The procedure is mentioned in
a famous hymn sometimes found in school hymn-books:

> 'We build like corals, grave by grave,
> A pathway climbing heavenwards.'

Corals are rather exacting in the conditions in which they will
live. They grow only in the top 150 feet or so of tropical waters,
the temperature of which must not fall below 68° F., and feed
on tiny organisms which float near the surface. They can survive out of the water only for short periods, and if the water
becomes laden with silt, they die.

* *Vik* is Norwegian for 'inlet'.

Once a bank of coral (a *reef*) has formed on a shelving beach, it grows most vigorously on the seaward side, where there is a greater supply of food, while on the landward side the rate of growth is much slower.

Types of Coral Reefs. Coral reefs take three main forms:

(i) *Fringing Reefs*, which consist of belts of coral separated from the coastline proper by shallow lagoons (Fig. 139*a*).

(ii) *Barrier Reefs*, the best example of which is the Great Barrier Reef stretching for over 1,500 miles along the north-east coast of Australia. It is separated from the mainland by a channel over 100 miles wide and about forty fathoms deep (Fig. 139*b*).

(iii) *Atolls*, which are roughly horseshoe-shaped areas of coral enclosing a central lagoon (Fig. 139*c*). On the inside of the reefs, sand and broken pieces of coral build up to form lines

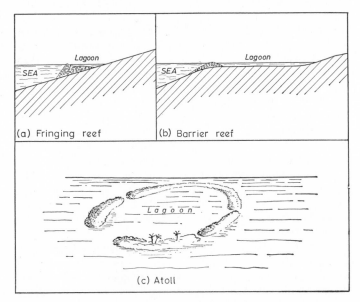

Fig. 139—Types of coral reef.

of dunes on which sometimes palm trees grow. These are the 'coral islands' which used to be so popular with writers of stories about shipwreck and buried treasure.

Theories of Coral Reef Formation. No one is quite sure how these coral coastlines have been formed. Indeed, the subject has been debated for nearly a century without any really satisfactory solution having been reached. Fringing reefs are fairly easily explained, but it is more difficult to see how barrier reefs and atolls have been formed, since they appear to rise from depths of ocean where the water is cold. It is also extremely unlikely that Nature would distribute over the ocean beds a vast number of little platforms 100 feet or so below sea-level, all conveniently situated for the growth of coral in the warm surface waters.

The Subsidence Theory. Charles Darwin, as a result of his famous voyage in H.M.S. *Beagle*, was, in 1842, the first to put forward a suggestion. The floor of the Pacific Ocean is known to be dotted with the cones of numerous extinct volcanoes. At one time, according to Darwin, the topmost portions of these volcanoes stood above the level of the ocean, and around them grew fringing reefs. Slowly the floor of the ocean subsided, and while this was going on, the coral reefs grew higher, particularly on the outsides, so that eventually the peaks of the volcanoes sank out of sight, leaving only the outer rims of the fringing reefs above the water (Fig. 140). Darwin thought that barrier reefs were also a kind of fringing reef, formed on the edges of subsiding platforms just off the mainland.

All this made quite good sense, but the suggestion that subsidence had taken place was only a guess on Darwin's part. Actually, it has since turned out to be a very good guess, because later research has shown that the earth's crust has in fact sagged in the Pacific area.

Other Theories. Various other suggestions have been made, but perhaps the most useful was the one put forward by an American geographer named R. A. Daly in 1910. At the height of the Ice Age the water must have been too cold to permit the growth of coral, and, in any case, the fall in sea-

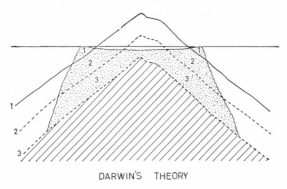

DARWIN'S THEORY

Fig. 140—The formation of an atoll by subsidence.

level would leave the existing reefs above the surface of the water. Wave action would then plane off the tops of the islands, leaving platforms on which the coral would again begin to grow when the water became warmer at the end of the Ice Age. As sea-level rose with the melting of the ice-sheets, so the coral would grow upwards. The truth of the matter may very well lie in a combination of Darwin's subsidence theory and Daly's 'Glacial Control' theory, but it is an extremely interesting problem.

CHAPTER ELEVEN

The Seas and Oceans

JUST over two-thirds of the surface of the earth is permanently covered by water. Some of it is, of course, to be found in rivers and lakes, and some of it in seas like the Mediterranean, the Baltic and the Caspian; but by far the greatest part of the *hydrosphere* is made up by the vast Pacific, Atlantic and Indian Oceans.

The Distribution of Land and Sea. The way in which Nature has distributed land and sea over the earth is rather strange. If you look at a school globe from somewhere above the North Pole instead of from the usual angle, you will find that the northern half (or *hemisphere*) is chiefly occupied by large land masses. If you then look at it from beyond the South Pole, you will see that the Southern Hemisphere is almost entirely made up of oceans, with only Antarctica, Australasia and the southern parts of South America and Africa to break the expanse of water. How this arrangement came about and why all the land masses taper off southwards has never been satisfactorily explained, although some interesting guesses have been made.

The Ocean Floors. At one time it was assumed that the floors of the oceans were flat and featureless, but we now know that there are hills and hollows almost the same as on the land. It was not until the possibility arose of laying a telegraph cable across the Atlantic that very much interest was shown in what was beneath the water. In any case, the only way that the depth of the sea could be found in those days was by letting down from a ship a weight on the end of a long wire. In the circumstances, it is not surprising that our knowledge was rather scanty. Nowadays, an instrument called an *echo-sounder* transmits from a ship vibrations which are reflected off the bed of the ocean and picked up again in the ship. The time taken by

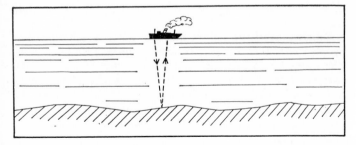

FIG. 141—Registering the depth of the sea by echo-sounding apparatus.

the vibration to do the double journey is recorded, and so automatically registers the depth (Fig. 141). This method is gradually being superseded by radar sounding.

The average depth of all the seas and oceans is about two and a half miles, but in some parts of the Pacific long trenches or deeps in the sea bed reach a depth of over five miles below the surface. Sections across the Pacific and Atlantic Oceans are shown in Fig. 142.

Temperature. In a very general way, the temperature at the surface of the oceanic waters decreases from the Equator, where it is about 80° F., to the polar regions, where it is almost at freezing point. But this is true only of the water near the surface. About a mile down the temperature is more or less the same at any latitude. Moreover, in various parts of the

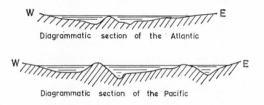

FIG. 142—Generalised sections across the Atlantic and Pacific Oceans.

oceans currents are warmer or colder than the surrounding waters.

Salinity. Everyone knows that sea water is salty, but few people realise that this salinity varies from one sea to another. The average salinity of sea water is 35 parts of salt in 1,000 parts of water. This is usually expressed as 35‰. The salinity of the main areas of ocean is round about this figure, but the Red Sea and Mediterranean have a salinity of 40‰, while the Baltic reaches only 7‰. In the Dead Sea the salinity is nearly 240‰.

As we saw in Chapter 5, the 'fresh' water of the rivers and streams contains various chemical substances (or mineral salts) derived from the rocks over and through which it has passed. Indeed, even rain water is not absolutely pure chemically. When salt water evaporates the salt is left behind; it seems fairly reasonable, therefore, to suggest that the oceans are like vast reservoirs in which for countless centuries the salt brought down by the rivers has been gradually accumulating. But the salts brought down by the rivers are not quite the same kind of salts as those found in the sea!

There is little doubt that in the seas themselves chemical processes are continually going on which not only add salts to the water, but also remove salts from it. For instance, many organisms, which will in time build up beds of limestone, take from the sea water some of the calcium carbonate with which to make their shells. The sea has, in fact, been described as a 'great chemical factory', making salt itself as well as receiving and altering the salts brought to it by the rivers.

In those parts of the ocean where the skies are clear and the sun's rays are most powerful, considerable quantities of water are evaporated. There is therefore a greater proportion of salt in the water left behind—in other words, the salinity is higher than the average of 35‰. But it is only slightly higher, because the waters of the large areas of ocean are constantly being mixed. Where rainfall is plentiful, the oceanic waters are diluted, and because of the masses of cloud the sun cannot evaporate the water so rapidly. The salinity is thus less than average.

The salinity of the seas which are, as it were, off-shoots of the main areas of ocean and, to some extent, shut in by land so that their waters cannot mix so freely with the ocean, is noticeably different from the 35‰ average. Whether it is higher or lower than 35‰ depends on how completely the sea is enclosed by land, the rate of evaporation, and the quantity of fresh water poured into it by the rivers. In the Red Sea, for instance, much of the water is evaporated by the hot sun, and there are very few rivers to reduce the salinity. But in the case of the Baltic Sea, rivers are numerous, and since the climate of the area is a cold one, very little evaporation takes place.

The Dead Sea is the centre of an area of *inland drainage*—in other words, it is not connected to the open sea. The water which reaches it can only sink into the ground or evaporate. The salt has therefore accumulated in the Dead Sea to such an extent that the salinity is nearly 240‰. When you were learning to swim, you probably noticed that you got along very much better in the sea than in the fresh water of your school swimming bath. Salt water is denser than fresh water, and in the Dead Sea it is almost impossible to sink. Salt lakes like Lake Eyre in Australia are at the centres of areas of inland drainage. Sometimes, after a long period without rain, the water evaporates altogether, leaving an area of salt about a foot thick to mark where the lake has been (see p. 90).

It is quite easy to extract ordinary 'common salt', which forms the greater part of all the material dissolved in sea water, by the simple process of evaporation. But sometimes Nature comes to our aid. Iodine, for example, is taken from the water by seaweed, which is then used as a fertiliser for the land. Scientific processes have been invented for extracting some minerals from sea water, such as magnesium, but no method has yet been discovered of 'winning' the countless other substances which it contains. It is estimated that we could obtain from the sea a large part of the minerals we now get by mining and quarrying—if only we could find out how to do it!

OCEAN CURRENTS

Fig. 143 shows in a simplified form the regular movements of the surface waters of the oceans. It is important to remember that the arrows on the diagram represent the drifts of water (or *currents*) at the surface only. These surface currents were discovered by the earliest navigators hundreds of years ago, and used by them in their voyages, but we still have a great deal to learn about the movements of the deeper waters.

The general pattern of surface currents in both the Pacific and Atlantic Oceans is like a vast figure 8, with its centre on the Equator. The direction of the various currents is easily remembered by drawing a figure 8 in the opposite way to that in which it is usually drawn. In the Indian Ocean the general pattern is the same, but the top half of the 8 is very much confined, and has one important peculiarity. Owing to the monsoon winds a seasonal reversal of the currents occurs; in June the flow is clockwise and in December anti-clockwise. Notice also the Equatorial Counter Currents and the West Wind Drift, which, since there is no land in the Southern Hemisphere to interrupt it, forms an unbroken band all round the globe.

The currents are named, in most cases, after the places near which they flow, and are very often either warmer or colder than the waters on each side of them. The waters of the Gulf Stream and the North Atlantic Drift, for example, come originally from the equatorial regions and are still comparatively warm by the time they reach Norway and the British Isles. But the waters of the Canaries Current on their journey towards the Equator are comparatively cool.

Facts such as these have an important bearing on climate. For instance, winters in Norway and the British Isles are by no means as cold as they would be without the North Atlantic Drift. Air warmed by contact with the waters of the Drift moves over these areas, and keeps them warmer in winter than they would normally be at so great a distance from the Equator. Moreover, the sea to the north never freezes, since the waters

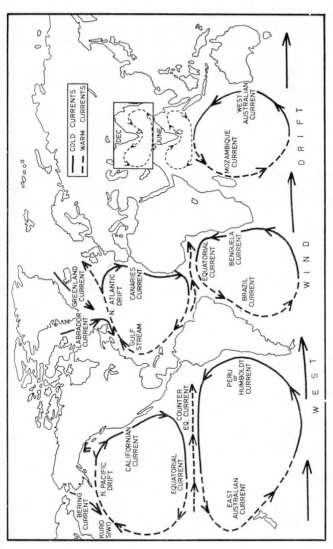

Fig. 143—Surface currents of the oceans (simplified).

are derived from the North Atlantic Drift. In comparable latitudes on the other side of the Atlantic, where a current of cold water from the polar regions flows past Labrador, the sea is frozen for a large part of the year.

The 'figure 8' circulation of the oceanic waters is due to a combination of causes. Differences in temperature, rate of evaporation and salinity, together with the direction of the prevailing winds and the rotation of the earth on its axis, all play their part in producing ocean currents, but a full explanation would be far too long and complicated for us to try to understand here. You could, however, get some idea of the sort of thing that happens in the oceans, if you tried the effect of gently pouring salt water, coloured with a few drops of cochineal or some red ink, into a glass tank containing fresh water.

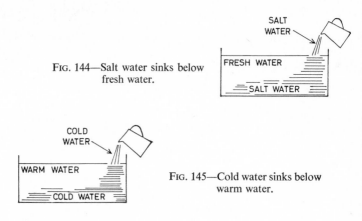

FIG. 144—Salt water sinks below fresh water.

FIG. 145—Cold water sinks below warm water.

FIG. 146—Currents caused by floating ice.

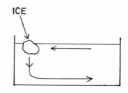

You would find that the salt water, because it was denser than the fresh water, would settle at the bottom of the tank (Fig. 144). Or you could pour cold coloured water on to warm water (Fig. 145). In this case, the cold water would find its way down to below the warm water. Put a block of ice in one end of a tank full of water, and you will create a downward current of water chilled by the ice and a current at the surface towards the ice, taking the place of the water which has sunk (Fig. 146).

Currents at the surface are clearly bound up with upward and downward movements of water, and when you remember how deep the oceans are, you will realise how little of the whole picture of oceanic circulation is presented by the surface currents.

THE TIDES

A similar situation exists with regard to the periodic rise and fall of the level of the seas and oceans that we refer to as tides. That a rough connection exists between the moon and the tides is as obvious to us when we are at the seaside as it was to coastal dwellers of ancient times. But although science can show that the gravitational attraction of the moon, and to a lesser extent that of the sun, are broadly responsible for causing these periodic fluctuations, the explanation of the exact pattern of vertical movements which result in the various areas of water is by no means as simple as was originally supposed.

The Influence of the Moon. In those parts of the seas and oceans which are for the time being facing the moon, a general heaping up of the water occurs (Fig. 147, *A*). There is also (for reasons too complicated to be explained here) a similar heaping up on the far side (*B*). At *C* and *D* the level of the water falls. As the earth spins on its axis, a given point in the ocean experiences in the course of any one day and night two periods of deep water and two of shallow. Since the moon travels in its orbit in the same direction as that in which the earth is spinning, 24 hours 50 minutes (or a *lunar day*) elapses before the succession of two high and two low tides begins again. You

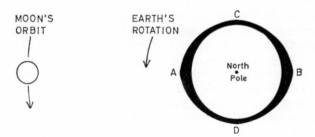

Fig. 147—The general effect of the gravitational attraction of the moon on the oceanic waters.

will probably remember hearing people at the seaside saying the 'the tide comes in about an hour later every day'. This, of course, is roughly true, and ignores the intervening high tide, which occurs, perhaps, during the night.

The Influence of the Sun. The sun also exerts a gravitational attraction on the oceanic waters; but although the sun is so much larger than the moon, it is very much farther away, and the resulting displacement of the water is less than half that caused by the moon. When the sun, earth and moon are in the same straight line (at Full Moon and New Moon), the sun and the moon 'pull' together; the high tides are particularly high, and the low tides are particularly low. These are known as *spring* tides. At other times they are not 'pulling' together, and the difference between high tide and low tide—called the *range* or *amplitude* of the tide—is less. At the Half Moon, when the sun and moon are 'pulling' at right angles to each other, the range is greatly reduced and we get *neap** tides (Figs. 148 and 149).

Progressive and Stationary Waves. It used to be thought that the high tides were the two enormous, very flat waves formed by the 'bulges' at *A* and *B* in Fig. 147, which travelled round the earth as it revolved. But as more and more measurements were made of the amplitude of the tide all over the world, it became obvious that, however many allowances were made for

* i.e. 'nipped'.

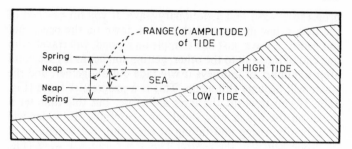

FIG. 148—The range (or amplitude) of spring tides and neap tides.

exceptions due to the irregular shapes of the ocean basins, the high tides did not behave as if they were in fact enormous *progressive* waves of this kind.

The present theory is that the main bodies of water on the earth can be divided into sections in which *stationary* waves rock under the influence of the sun and moon.

Two simple experiments with the tanks used in connection with ocean currents will demonstrate the difference between a

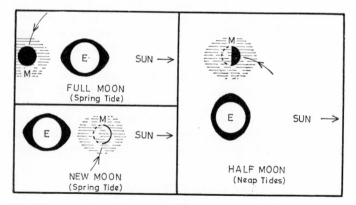

FIG. 149—The effect of the combined gravitational attraction of the sun and moon upon the oceanic waters during the varying phases of the moon.

progressive wave and a stationary wave. If you lift one end of the tank a few inches, and then let it down on the bench not too gently, a wave, just like a ripple on a pond, will travel from one end of the tank to the other, getting smaller as it goes, until after a number of journeys it will fade out altogether, and the water will become still again. This is a progressive wave (Fig. 150). If you now lift the tank as before, but this time let it down on the bench very slowly and carefully, the water will rock bodily, rising and falling at each end, but remaining at the same height in the centre. This is a stationary wave (Fig. 151).

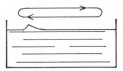

FIG. 150—A progressive wave.

FIG. 151—A stationary wave.

The rise and fall of the water in the main ocean areas seems to be caused more by stationary waves than by progressive waves. It may help you to visualise the situation if you imagine a vast fairground covered entirely by see-saws with their ends tied together, and all perpetually rocking in concert under the gravitational attraction of the sun and moon.

Bores. It is, however, admitted that progressive waves may form in shallow or restricted areas. The bore, a foaming wall of water several feet high, which at certain times advances up the estuary of the River Severn, is caused by a progressive wave which forms in the gradually narrowing channel. The Trent *egre* and the Seine *mascaret* are formed in the same way.

THE CONTINENTAL SHELF

One very strange feature of certain parts of the seas and oceans has been left till the end of this chapter and given a section to itself because it provides the world with such a large proportion of its food supply.

If you were to sail westwards from Ireland in a ship fitted with echo-sounding equipment, you would find that for the first hundred miles or so the apparatus would record depths of no more than 600 feet. Then, quite suddenly, readings would be obtained of two miles or so. Apart from a rise of the sea bed in the centre of the Atlantic, readings of about this depth would be continued until you came close to the coast of Canada, when, equally suddenly, depths of 500 or 600 feet would again be recorded (Fig. 152). Platforms at roughly this depth form seaward extensions of certain of the great land masses, and together are known as the continental shelf. This feature is something of a geological puzzle. It may have been built up by deposition, or it may have been caused by erosion, but neither of these explanations is really satisfactory. To mention only one problem in particular, it is difficult to see why, if the shelf has been built by the deposition of material, there should be such a steep *continental slope* on the outside edge. Probably the shelf is the submerged margins of a formerly more extensive continent.

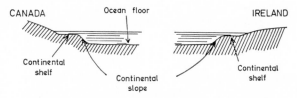

FIG. 152—The Atlantic continental shelf.

The shelf is especially wide on both sides of the North Atlantic; in fact, the British Isles is really situated on a part of the continental shelf which extends westwards from the mainland of Europe. The large islands to the north of Australia (the Philippines, New Guinea, etc.) are situated on a wide platform in much the same way, but, apart from this area, the Pacific Ocean is almost without a continental shelf.

The importance of the continental shelf to mankind is that although fish of one sort or another are to be found in practically all the waters of the globe, they are particularly abundant in the large areas of shallow water which the shelf provides. Fish feed on *plankton*—that is, minute plants and animals which float or drift around in the water—and in most cases they lay their eggs or spawn on the sea bed. Beyond the edge of the continental shelf conditions are not at all favourable to life. Sunlight reaches down into the water only for about 500 feet, and, besides being dark, the deeper waters are very cold. The continental shelf, therefore, provides convenient breeding grounds and plentiful supplies of fish food, and the shallowness of the water helps the operation of fishing.

Where two currents meet over the continental shelf, plankton is even more abundant. This is one of the reasons why so many fish inhabit the waters off Newfoundland. Another is that eroded material, embedded in the icebergs which are carried southwards by the Labrador Current, sinks to the bottom when the icebergs melt on meeting the warm waters of the Gulf Stream. The material dropped by the melting icebergs has over the years piled up to form the Grand Banks, making the sea on the continental shelf at this point shallower still, and so even more suitable as a spawning ground (Fig. 153). The Dogger Bank in the North Sea has also been built up by deposition; this area too is a notable breeding ground. The three most important fishing areas in the world are the North Sea, the Newfoundland Banks and the Sea of Japan, all situated on parts of the continental shelf.

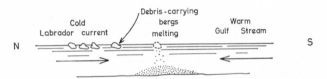

FIG. 153—The formation of the Grand Banks off Newfoundland.

CHAPTER TWELVE

The Atmosphere

IT is all too easy for us to take the atmosphere for granted. We cannot see it, and we can feel it and hear it only when the wind blows in our faces or whistles in the trees and telephone wires. Yet it is a very vital part of our existence on the earth. Without air we could not breathe, and it is the changes and movements in the atmosphere that produce for us the sunny days and the wet days, the clouds and the fogs, the gales and the thunderstorms—in fact, all those things which make up our weather and our climate.

THE COMPOSITION OF THE ATMOSPHERE

The atmosphere consists of a mixture of gases. Over three-quarters of it is nitrogen, nearly a quarter of it is oxygen, there is a little carbon dioxide, and minute traces of helium, argon and some other rare gases (Fig. 154). By far the most important of these is, of course, oxygen. It is absorbed by our bodies when we breathe, and you will almost certainly have read at some time or another of people with lung complaints being put in 'oxygen tents', where more oxygen can be fed into their bodies than they could take from the air around them. The nitrogen, although greater in quantity, is by no means as useful. Fertilisers and explosives can, however, be made from it.

It is impossible to give an exact figure for the height of the atmosphere, since the air becomes more and more rarefied as we move farther away from the earth's surface, but for all practical purposes there is so little air left fifteen miles or so above the earth that we may consider the atmosphere to be about fifteen miles high.

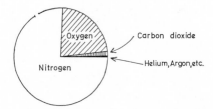

F<small>IG</small>. 154—The composition of the atmosphere.

THE PRESSURE OF THE ATMOSPHERE

We sometimes talk about things being 'as light as air', so you will probably find it very difficult to believe that the air in a normal-sized classroom weighs about four hundredweights— the combined weight of four or five 15-year old boys or girls.* Since the air has weight, it must necessarily press upon the surface of the earth. The average pressure at sea-level is 14·7 lb. per square inch—which means that the column of air above your head and shoulders weighs about half a ton! If you climb to the top of a mountain, the column of air above your head will be less than fifteen miles high, and the pressure will be less than 14·7 lb. per square inch. Moreover, the pressure in the same place varies from one day to another.

The Mercury Barometer. It has been known how to measure these variations in pressure ever since 1643, when the great scientist Galileo invented the barometer. He (or rather his assistant, Torricelli, for Galileo was then blind) filled a long glass tube with mercury, put his thumb over the open end, turned it upside down, and placed the open end in a bowl of mercury. When he took his thumb away, the mercury in the tube did not run down into the bowl, but remained in the tube, with the top level of the mercury about $29\frac{1}{2}$ inches above the mercury in the bowl (Fig. 155). Galileo explained this by saying that the pressure of the air upon the mercury in the bowl sup-

* You can, if you like, work it out for yourself. A cubic foot of air at sea-level normally weighs $1\frac{1}{4}$ ounces.

ported the column of mercury in the tube. To put it another way, the pressure exerted by a layer of air eleven miles high is equal to the pressure exerted by a layer of mercury $29\frac{1}{2}$ inches thick. It would be possible to perform this experiment with some other liquid, but you would need a very much longer tube, since mercury is the heaviest liquid known. If you used water, the tube would have to be over 30 feet long.

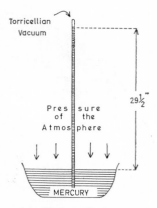

FIG. 155—Galileo's experiment illustrating the pressure of the atmosphere.

The Aneroid Barometer. The original mercury barometer is obviously a large and cumbersome instrument, and although it is still used in laboratories and weather stations, where great accuracy is required, a much lighter and more portable piece of equipment, known as the aneroid* barometer, was subsequently invented. This consists of a small metal container, which has had most of the air drawn out of it before being sealed by a little blob of solder, and has a kind of lid made of very thin metal. The higher the atmospheric pressure on the outside of the container, the more the lid is pushed inwards; when the pressure is lower, the lid springs outwards. These in and out movements of the lid are transferred to a pointer on a dial (Figs. 156 and 157). This is the type of barometer which forms an almost traditional article of hall furniture. The numbers on the dial still represent inches of mercury, although no mercury is used in the construction.

Barometric Readings and the Weather. It was realised quite soon after the invention of the first barometer that the height of the mercury in the tube varied with the weather. On a fine day the atmospheric pressure tended to be slightly higher than normal, and the mercury was pushed up the tube to about 30

* *Aneroid* comes from two Greek words which mean 'not wet'.

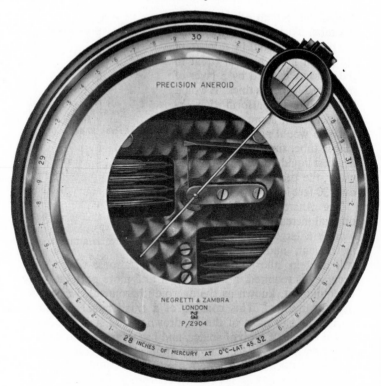

Fig. 156—A precision-type aneroid barometer.

inches above the mercury in the bowl, but when it rained, the
pressure tended to be lower, and the column was only about
29 inches in height. The whole thing seemed so obvious that
towards the end of the seventeenth century a certain Robert
Hooke made up the familiar scale, from 'Stormy' at 28 inches
to 'Very Dry' at 31 inches, which has appeared on ordinary
aneroid barometers ever since.

For nearly 300 years people have regarded these descriptions

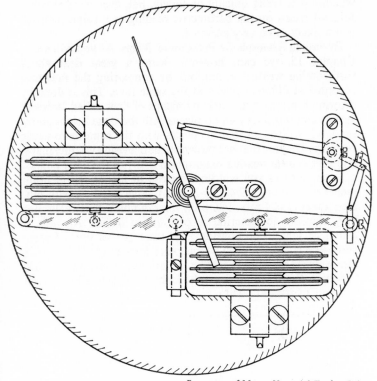

By courtesy of Messrs. Negretti & Zambra, Ltd.

FIG. 157—The mechanism of the aneroid barometer shown on the opposite page.

on the dial as a kind of weather forecast—with very little justification. The connection between the 'height' of the barometer and the weather is much more complicated than was originally supposed. It is true that some of the modern aneroid barometers have somewhat lengthy instructions printed on them; the weather 'forecast' is, for instance, quite different according to whether the pointer is rising or falling, and whether it is rising quickly or slowly, but, even so, a weather forecast based on the barometric reading at a single 'station' is not likely to be very accurate.

Recording Atmospheric Pressure on Maps. As you will see in Chapter 15, we can, however, learn a great deal about forthcoming weather conditions by comparing the pressures recorded at different places at the same time. This is done by drawing a pressure 'picture' by means of lines called *isobars*.* Just as contour lines join up places with the same height above sea-level, so isobars join up places with the same barometric pressure. They are the lines shown on the television weather maps, and on the little weather diagrams in many of the daily papers.

In some cases you will find, instead of figures representing inches of mercury (29·4″, 30·2″, etc.), large numbers with mb. after them (1,004 mb., 986 mb., for example). It is really not very sensible to describe a pressure in inches. An inch is a unit of length. So nowadays we use a proper unit of pressure—the *millibar* (or *mb.*)—and, very fortunately, the average atmospheric pressure in temperate latitudes is just about 1,000 millibars, thus the figures on the isobars are generally between 950 and 1,050† (Fig. 158).

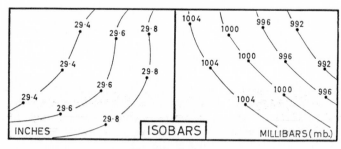

Fig. 158—Isobars.

* You will come across a number of other words beginning with *iso*. *Isos* is Greek for 'equal', and these 'iso' lines are all 'lines joining up places of equal something or other'; e.g. *isobar* means 'line joining up places of equal barometric pressure'.

† You can convert inches of mercury to millibars by multiplying by 33·9.

The Measurement of Height. The barometer is also used for measuring heights. As you go up a mountain, the column of air above your head gets shorter, and the pressure, therefore, gets less. At a height of 800 feet the pressure is about 1 inch of mercury (or 33·9 mb.) less than at the foot of the mountain. Tiny aneroid barometers the size of pocket watches are carried by climbers, and, providing they have remembered to 'set' their instruments before starting the ascent, they can read off their height at any point in their climb. The altimeter in an aircraft works on the same principle.

THE TEMPERATURE OF THE ATMOSPHERE

Radiation and Conduction. As the pilot of an aircraft rises farther above the surface of the earth, he not only finds that the atmospheric pressure decreases, he also finds that the temperature gets lower and lower. There are two reasons for this. In the first place, when the pressure upon a gas (in this case a mixture of gases—the air) is reduced, it automatically expands and gets colder. Take the valve out of your bicycle tyre and hold your hand over the hole as the air rushes out, and you will have no doubt that this is true. Conversely, when the air is compressed, it gets warmer. The bottom of the bicycle pump near the connection gets quite warm when you pump up the tyre. In the second place, the air is heated by contact with the ground, so that, except in special circumstances, the warmest air is that which is closest to the ground. The process by which heat is transferred from one thing to another when they are touching is called conduction. When heat is sent out by one object and taken in by another some distance away, the process is called radiation. The sun heats the ground by radiation, and the ground in turn heats the air by conduction. The sun does *not* heat the air as its rays pass through it.

The temperature drops about $3\frac{1}{2}°$ F. on an average for every 1,000 feet as you go up a mountain. Only a few miles from the little coastal town of Fort William in Scotland is Ben Nevis, the highest mountain in the British Isles, 4,406 feet above sea-

level. At its summit the temperature is about 15° F. lower than
it is at Fort William. In Africa, very close to the Equator, is
Mount Kilimanjaro, nearly 20,000 feet above sea-level. At the
top of this mountain the temperature is about 60° F. lower
than at the bottom, and the air is so thin that you would have
the greatest difficulty in finding enough oxygen (and hence
energy) to enable you to climb among the snow and ice with
which the upper parts are covered.

The Thermometer. Temperature is measured by means of a
thermometer. You will almost certainly be familiar with the
usual kind of thermometer, in which mercury in a little bulb
expands with increasing temperature and rises up a fine glass
tube; there may be a thermometer of this type in your classroom. You will notice that it is marked in degrees *Fahrenheit*
(° F.), and that the freezing point is 32°. On this scale the
boiling point of water is 212°, but thermometers used for
measuring the temperature of the air are made to go up to
only about 130°. There are many other kinds of thermometers,
and a number of other scales as well. The doctor takes the
temperatures of his patients with a special 'clinical' thermometer containing mercury like the one described above, but
the 'temperature gauge' on the dashboard of a car records the
temperature of the water in the radiator by means of a strip
of metal which expands as the water gets warmer. In Physics
lessons you use mercury thermometers with degrees *Centigrade*
marked on them. (See note, page 182.)

Actually, it is very difficult to take the temperature of the air.
The difficulty lies in the fact that, if you are not very careful
where you place the thermometer, it will not give a true recording of the air temperature. If you let the sun on a warm day
shine directly on the thermometer, you will get a reading of
about 120° F. Put it in a confined space, where the air cannot
circulate, and you will get a low reading. Put it against the outside wall of a room in which a fire is burning, and again the
reading will be inaccurate. Lay it on the ground, and you will
be measuring the temperature of the ground, not the air—and
so on. For the reading to be really accurate, the thermometer

must be in the shade, hanging clear of walls, and with the air continually circulating round it.

The Stevenson Screen. To be sure of getting a really accurate reading, the weather stations use a kind of box on stilts called a Stevenson screen. You can sometimes see one of these surrounded by a fence in a park or public garden at, for instance, a seaside resort. The Stevenson screen looks very much like a beehive, has 'louvred' sides which let the air through but keep out the direct rays of the sun. The ground beneath is covered with grass, to prevent reflection. There is no proper 'floor' to the box, and the various instruments, including the thermometer, are hung on hooks inside (Fig. 159).

It is often extremely useful to know the highest and lowest temperatures reached during any period of twenty-four hours. Your local newspaper may, in fact, tell you what these—the *maximum* and *minimum* temperatures—were for the previous

By courtesy of Messrs. Negretti & Zambra, Ltd.

FIG. 159- -A standard Stevenson screen.

day. You may have wondered, seeing these figures in the news-paper, whether somebody had to stand by the thermometer all day and all night watching it. Fortunately, there is no need for anyone to undertake such a thankless task. Inside the Stevenson screen are two thermometers of special design. In one of these a constriction of the tube just above the bulb prevents the mercury from falling back after it has reached the maximum temperature, and in the other spirit is used in place of mercury and a small piece of steel records the lowest point reached by the contracting alcohol.

Recording Temperature on Maps. Just as we drew pressure 'patterns' by means of isobars, so we can draw temperature 'patterns' by joining up all places with the same temperature (Fig. 160). Such lines are called *isotherms*.

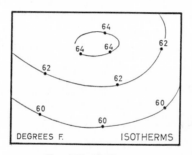

FIG. 160—Isotherms.

When temperature 'patterns' like the one in the diagram are drawn, it is necessary to 'reduce' the temperatures of the actual places 'to sea-level'. In other words, the temperatures shown on the map are the temperatures which would be recorded if the places were at sea-level. If a place is, for instance, actually at 1,000 feet above sea-level, the tempera-ture figure given on the map will be about $3\frac{1}{2}°$ F. higher than the temperature recorded by the thermometer. If we did not do this, the isotherms would be merely a repetition of the contour lines on the physical map.

MOVEMENTS WITHIN THE ATMOSPHERE—WINDS

The Relation of Pressure to Winds. The air is, of course, never absolutely still. When air moves from one part of the earth's surface to another, we say that a wind is blowing.

Winds are caused by the differences in temperature between one place and another, in the following way:

Let us suppose that, for one reason or another, the ground at *A* in Fig. 161 has become warmer than the ground at *B*. Heat from the ground will make the air over *A* warmer than the air over *B*. The air at *A* will therefore expand, become lighter, and rise, forming an upward current; the air from *B* will now move in to take its place—or, to put it another way, a wind will blow from *B* to *A*. Over *B* there will be a downward movement of air.

There are two further points to notice:

(i) The upward movement of the air at *A* is known as a convection current. *Convection* is the name given to the way in which heat is transferred from one part of a body of gas or liquid to another. It is the process by which the hot air around a fire is carried up the chimney, and the process by which the water warmed by your back-boiler or domestic boiler is carried up to the hot water tank in the bathroom cupboard.

(ii) The barometer at *A*, where the air is rising, will record a lower pressure than it will at *B*. *A* is therefore said to be a *low-pressure area* and *B* a *high-pressure area.* If the difference in pressure between any two places is very great, the wind will be strong, but if the difference is only slight, the movement of air will be slower, and we shall call it, perhaps, a light breeze.

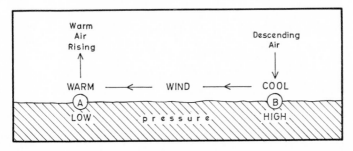

FIG. 161—Conditions leading to the horizontal movement of air, i.e. wind

Land and Sea Breezes. When you are on holiday at the sea-side, you will almost certainly find that during daytime, particularly if the sun is shining, the air is moving off the sea. This is because land heats up more quickly than water. In the morning, as the land warms up, it becomes a low-pressure area, the air over it rises, and the air from the comparatively cool sea moves in to the land as the familiar sea breeze or on-shore wind (Fig. 162).

At night-time things are reversed. Although during the day the land warms up very quickly, it is only too anxious to throw off its heat at night. The sea on the other hand is slower both in heating up during the day and in cooling down at night. So usually during the night the air over the sea is warmer than the air over the land. It is now, therefore, the land which is the high pressure area, and the air moves from land to sea in the form of a land breeze or off-shore wind (Fig. 163).

This strange eagerness of the land to warm up and cool down, and the reluctance of the sea to do the same, is responsible for one of the most important wind-systems in the world —the *monsoon* winds of South-East Asia—which are really only land and sea breezes on a vast scale. You will hear more about this in Chapter 14.

If your school has an open-air swimming bath, you will undoubtedly have had ample proof of what in your Physics lessons is called the different *specific heats* of land and sea. When the weather turns cold after a hot spell, the water seems surprisingly warm when you eventually pluck up courage to dive in. On a really hot day the water sometimes seems surprisingly cold.

Recording the Wind. The ordinary weathercock seen on church spires and other high buildings records the direction of the wind, and it is very important to remember that a wind is named after the point of the compass from which it comes. A west wind, for example, blows from west to east. The speed of the wind is recorded in miles per hour by means of various types of *anemometer*. The one most commonly used looks like four half tennis balls on the end of a shaft connected to a dial

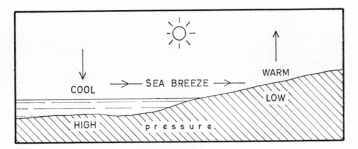

FIG. 162—The formation of a sea breeze or on-shore wind.

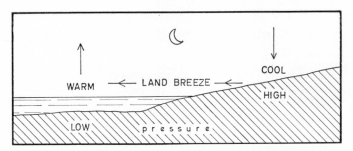

FIG. 163—The formation of a land breeze or off-shore wind.

(Fig. 164). The pressure exerted by the wind is of vital importance to designers of buildings, bridges and aeroplanes, and in
a gale can be very considerable.

WATER VAPOUR IN THE ATMOSPHERE

The air is never absolutely dry. It always contains particles of
invisible water vapour. The precise amount varies from place to
place and from time to time, but on the average the air in an
ordinary school classroom probably contains about 3 or 4 lb.
of water vapour.

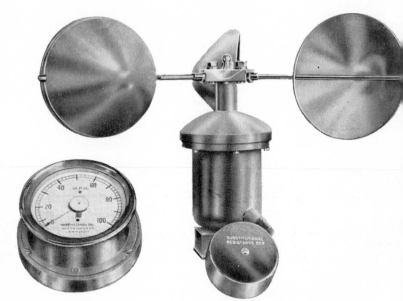

By courtesy of Messrs. Negretti & Zambra, Ltd.

Fig. 164—A generator-type cup anemometer. In this type of anemometer the voltage which arises from the rotation of the spindle on which the cups are mounted is used as a measure of the speed of the wind and is indicated on a voltmeter calibrated in miles per hour and connected to the instrument by a length of electric cable.

If there were no water vapour in the atmosphere, there would be no rain or snow, no hail, no clouds—and no fog. It is therefore of particular interest and importance to the geographer, since all these things affect our lives to a very great extent.

Relative Humidity. In practice, it is of hardly any use to us to know how many pounds or tons of water vapour the air contains. What is, however, of very great use is to know how much water vapour any particular 'parcel' of air contains compared with the amount it could contain. This is called its relative humidity.* The quantity of water vapour the air can hold depends on its temperature; the warmer it is, the more it can hold. If at any particular temperature the air contains only half what it could contain, we say that the relative humidity is 50 per cent.; if it contains almost as much as it could contain, the relative humidity would be, perhaps, 98 per cent., and so on. If the air is just full of water vapour, we say that it is *saturated*, and if, for some reason, more water vapour still is added to it, the extra water vapour condenses and forms droplets of water. Moreover, if a parcel of air gets colder, it may well be that it contains more water vapour than it can hold at the lower temperature; so, again, the extra water vapour is thrown out as water.

When the water vapour in the air 'overflows' in this way—that is, *condenses*—we get cloud, rain, snow, hail or fog. If, therefore, we know that the relative humidity of the air over the British Isles, for instance, is high—if the air is, in fact, near to the point of 'overflowing'—we can make a shrewd guess that, if it is disturbed at all, we may well have to cancel tomorrow's cricket match.

Recording Relative Humidity. The relative humidity is measured by a hygrometer, which consists of two small thermometers placed side by side. The bulb of one of them is kept wet by a piece of muslin trailing in a bowl of water (Fig. 165). This thermometer, because of the wet muslin, always shows a lower temperature than the dry one, unless the air is saturated. We read off the two temperatures registered by the thermometers and then look up the relative humidity from a specially prepared table printed on a card which accompanies the instrument.

Your own hair grows longer when the atmosphere is moist! Pine cones, seaweed, birds flying low in the sky, cows retreating under the trees, are all reputed to give indications of increasing humidity and the approach of rain.

Types of Rainfall. There are three ways in which air is made to throw off its excess water vapour.

* This means 'comparative wetness'.

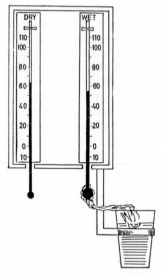

FIG. 165—A hygrometer.

(i) The air may be forced to rise over high ground. As it rises, it gets cooler, and eventually the temperature is reached at which the relative humidity is 100 per cent. As the air rises still farther, minute droplets of water form in the atmosphere. They are too small and light to fall to the ground, and so remain as cloud. If the droplets become so numerous and so crowded together that they bump into one another and join up, water droplets form which are too heavy to remain suspended in the air. These now fall as rain, which, in this case, since it is really caused by the relief of the land, is known as *relief rain* (Fig. 166*a*). Much of the rainfall experienced in Wales and on the western side of Scotland is of this type. By the time the air has passed over the mountains, a great deal of its water vapour has fallen as rain. Moreover, as it is now descending and getting warmer, it can more easily hold its water vapour. The area on the far side of the mountains, where rainfall is less, is said to be in the *rain shadow*.

(ii) Cold air is denser and heavier than warm air. If, therefore, a parcel of warm air meets a parcel of cold air, it will be forced upwards by the cold air. The result is just the same as if it had been forced to rise by a mountain. Rain caused in this way is called *frontal* (*depressional* or *cyclonic*) *rainfall*, since it occurs in association with 'fronts' in the depressions we so often hear about in the B.B.C. Weather Forecasts (Fig. 166*b*, see also Chapter 15).

(iii) The third kind of rainfall is known as *convection rain.*

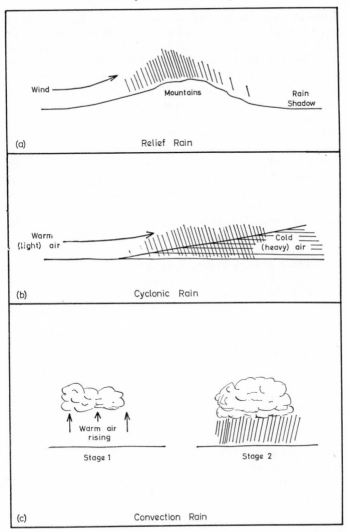

FIG. 166—Types of rainfall.

If the air over one part of the earth's surface becomes much warmer than the surrounding air, a convection current is set up, and the air rises vertically (Fig. 166c). In the Tropics and in thunderstorms elsewhere convection currents may reach speeds of nearly a hundred miles an hour. As the air rises, it is, of course, cooled, water vapour condenses, and eventually drops of rain, usually of considerable size, fall to the ground. This is, in fact, the kind of rainfall that we associate with a sudden 'heavy shower' or 'thunder-shower', and is quite distinct from the steady 'drizzle' of depressional rain.

The Measurement of Rainfall. Rainfall is measured in inches by means of a *rain-gauge*. When we say that an inch of rain has fallen, we mean that, if none of it had run away, sunk into the ground or been evaporated, it would cover the ground to a depth of 1 inch. It is as well that it does disperse in this way. If it did not, most places in the British Isles would at the end of the year find themselves under 2 or 3 feet of water! On a really wet day in Britain about half an inch of rain falls. When you are out of doors in such a downpour, you will probably think this is a surprisingly low figure, but you can easily prove it by leaving a tin out in the garden, and measuring the depth of water it collects.*

The rain gauge is really very much the same sort of thing—a tall, metal canister either 5 or 8 inches in diameter let into the ground, so that (for one reason alone) it cannot be knocked over. The rain is caught in a funnel resting in the top of the canister, and runs down into a bottle (Fig. 167). Once a day the contents (if any) of the can are emptied into a special measuring glass on which fractions of an inch are marked. We have to be very careful that the rain-gauge is not in the shelter of a house or a wall; and it is important that no water is allowed to splash up into the funnel after hitting the ground.

Rainfall may be recorded on maps by *isohyets*—that is, lines joining up places of equal rainfall.

* You would probably be equally surprised at the weight of the water which falls as rain. One inch of rain on a football pitch weighs nearly 200 tons!

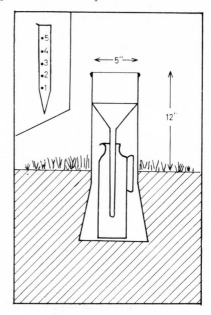

FIG. 167—A rain-gauge. The measuring cylinder which accompanies the instrument is tapered at the bottom so that very small amounts can be measured more accurately.

Snow. If the water vapour condenses when the temperature is already below freezing point, spicules of ice will form instead of water. These will collect into the tiny 'bundles' of frozen water vapour known as snowflakes. Seen under a microscope the ice crystals of a snowflake can be incredibly beautiful, but few of them reach the ground without becoming damp and so losing something of their sharp outline. Snow which has partly melted by the time it reaches the ground is known as *sleet*.

The rain-gauge is also used to measure the amount of snow which has fallen. The snow, of course, chokes the funnel of the instrument* but is subsequently melted so that it runs down the funnel into the measuring-glass. A foot of snow is roughly equal to 1 inch of rainfall.

* In areas where snow is particularly common, a special kind of rain-gauge is used, with a tall cylinder above the funnel.

Clouds. If the particles of water vapour 'thrown out' by the atmosphere are not plentiful enough or crowded enough to join up into raindrops or snowflakes, they may accumulate above the earth's surface in the form of clouds. Their shape, form, height and movements give the modern meteorologist a great deal of information about what is happening in the atmosphere and provide much of the evidence on which weather forecasts are based.

Clouds are classified partly by the height at which they form and partly by their appearance. About 100 years ago, a London chemist called Luke Howard divided clouds into four kinds, to which he gave Latin names—*cirrus* (meaning 'a wisp or lock of hair'), *stratus* ('a sheet'), *cumulus* ('a heap') and *nimbus* ('a rain-cloud'). These 'key-words' are used in combinations to make up the ten type-names in general use today. These are shown in Fig. 168, which also shows the height at which the various types are found.

Cirrus clouds form above 20,000 feet, where the atmosphere is so cold that the water vapour has turned to spicules of ice. The isolated cirrus cloud does, in fact, look like a 'wisp' in the sky, but *cirrostratus* is a thin sheet resembling a veil, which sometimes gives the sun or moon a halo. *Cirrocumulus* forms in ripples, providing the familiar 'mackerel' sky.

The prefix 'alto' signifies medium height, i.e. between 10,000 and 20,000 feet above the earth. *Altostratus* cloud gives the sky a watery appearance and the sun shines through it faintly, as if it were behind a sheet of ground glass; while *altocumulus* clouds (Fig. 169) form 'flattened, globular masses' arranged in lines or waves.

Stratocumulus is a low cloud and very much resembles alto-cumulus, except that the rolls or waves are much heavier looking and often show light and dark shading. *Stratus* cloud is like a dense fog several hundred feet above ground, and, for this reason, can be very annoying and even dangerous to hikers and climbers. *Nimbostratus* is the kind of cloud from which continuous rain or snow falls. It forms a dark grey layer which is often torn by the wind into shreds of 'scud'.

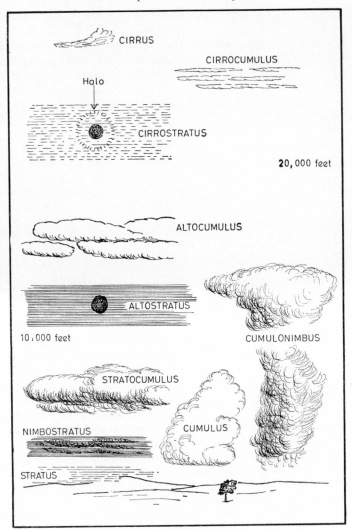

FIG. 168—Types of clouds.

Eric Kay

FIG. 169—Altocumulus clouds.

The two remaining types are not confined to any one layer of the atmosphere. *Cumulus* clouds (Fig. 170) are great white heaps with rounded tops and flat bases. Against the sun they may look grey with bright edges. They are often extremely tall and are usually associated with fine weather. In them the air is rising rapidly. Travellers by air will recollect how an aircraft suddenly rises and falls on entering and leaving each cloud. The *cumulonimbus* cloud has a low, ragged base, reaches tremendous heights, and almost always has a top which spreads out so that it resembles an anvil. Vertical currents within the cloud are of very great velocity. It has a dark and angry appearance and produces lightning, thunder and hail.

It is almost impossible to describe clouds by mere words. In your Geography Library, however, there are sure to be books

FIG. 170—Cumulus clouds.

devoted entirely to meteorology in which you will find photographs of all the various types of clouds. You should consult these and then go out of doors and try to identify them in the sky.

Fog and Mist.* These are exactly the same as cloud except that they occur at lower levels.

One type of fog which is very common in early autumn is known as *radiation fog*, and is caused by an *inversion of temperature*. When a warm, sunny day precedes a cool, still night, the air is suddenly chilled by contact with the ground and the

---

* There is no real difference between *fog* and *mist*, but in a fog 'visibility is less'—in other words, you cannot see so far through it. The official dividing line is at one kilometre.

water vapour is condensed. The air higher up remains fairly warm. Instead of the normal steady decrease of temperature with increasing height we therefore get a sudden decrease followed by a slight increase before normal conditions are resumed above the inversion. This is shown diagrammatically in Fig. 171.

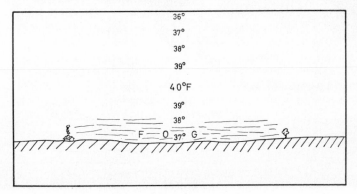

FIG. 171—The formation of radiation fog.

If particles of dust or smoke are hanging about in the air—as, for instance, in towns where there are many factories—fogs seem to form much more readily. The London 'pea-souper' of Charles Dickens' time very rarely happens nowadays, because modern house and factory chimneys do not throw out such dense, yellow smoke, but one can still hear in B.B.C. Weather Forecasts that 'fog will form in industrial areas'.

Dew. The same set of weather conditions is responsible for the formation of dew as for fog. In this case the water vapour condenses as droplets of water on the surface of some solid object. As was the case with snow, the water vapour may turn directly into tiny crystals of ice without first condensing into water. The result will be *hoar-frost*.

Hail. Hail is commonly formed in a strong convection current, and is really quite remarkable. The next time you experience a shower of hail, cut a hailstone in half before it can melt. You will find it is composed of layers of ice, rather like the layers in an onion. Before it reaches the ground, a hailstone may have been up and down in the atmosphere a number of times, each time collecting more moisture which freezes on it. Sometimes hailstones reach enormous sizes in this way. On September 22nd, 1935, hailstones the size of tennis balls were reported to have fallen near Northampton, and in tropical climates even larger ones have been known to fall. Market gardeners who own extensive greenhouses quite frequently insure them against damage by hailstones.

Thunder and Lightning. Although thunder and lightning may at first sight seem to have little to do with the presence of water vapour in the atmosphere, that is, in fact, the case. In a way which is still, after many years of research, not fully under-

FIG. 172—A spectacular flash of lightning over Jacksonville, Florida.

Ewing Galloway, N.Y.

stood, the strong convection currents which are always associated with thunderstorms cause the clouds to become charged with both positive and negative charges of electricity. Thunder-clouds are really like vast dynamos generating electricity with a pressure of millions of volts. When the electricity 'jumps the gap' between one cloud and another, or between a cloud and the ground, flashes of lightning are produced (Fig. 172). It is thought that the thunder is produced (but once again scientists are not quite sure) when the air rushes in to fill the partial vacuum created by the heating and expansion of the air in the flash of lightning.

Note: Temperature readings are now (1966) being issued by the Meteorological Office on both the Centigrade and Fahrenheit scales. For the benefit of readers who wish to convert the Fahrenheit figures in the text to Centigrade a conversion table is appended below.

F.	C.	F.	C.	F.	C.	F.	C.
130	54·4	75	23·9	44	6·7	13	−10·6
		74	23·3	43	6·1	12	−11·1
120	48·9	73	22·8	42	5·6	11	−11·7
		72	22·2	41	5	10	−12·2
110	43·3	71	21·7	40	4·4	9	−12·8
		70	21·1	39	3·9	8	−13·3
100	37·8	69	20·6	38	3·3	7	−13·9
99	37·2	68	20	37	2·8	6	−14·4
98	36·7	67	19·4	36	2·2	5	−15
97	36·1	66	18·9	35	1·7	4	−15·6
96	35·6	65	18·3	34	1·1	3	−16·1
95	35	64	17·8	33	0·6	2	−16·7
94	34·4	63	17·2	32	0	1	−17·2
93	33·9	62	16·7	31	−0·6	0	−17·8
92	33·3	61	16·1	30	−1·1	−1	−18·3
91	32·8	60	15·6	29	−1·7	−2	−18·9
90	32·2	59	15	28	−2·2	−3	−19·4
89	31·7	58	14·4	27	−2·8	−4	−20
88	31·1	57	13·9	26	−3·3	−5	−20·6
87	30·6	56	13·3	25	−3·9	−6	−21·1
86	30	55	12·8	24	−4·4	−7	−21·7
85	29·4	54	12·2	23	−5	−8	−22·2
84	28·9	53	11·7	22	−5·6	−9	−22·8
83	28·3	52	11·1	21	−6·1	−10	−23·3
82	27·8	51	10·6	20	−6·7		
81	27·2	50	10	19	−7·2	−20	−28·9
80	26·7	49	9·4	18	−7·8		
79	26·1	48	8·9	17	−8·3	−40	−40
78	25·6	47	8·3	16	−8·9		
77	25	46	7·8	15	−9·4	−60	−51·1
76	24·4	45	7·2	14	−10		

CHAPTER THIRTEEN

The Movements of the Earth in Space

IN Chapters 14 and 15 we shall be considering the various events which take place in the atmosphere under the headings of Climate and Weather. Since these depend to such a large extent upon the movements of the earth on its journey round the sun, it will be convenient in this present chapter to review these movements in so far as they bear upon the problem.

Comparative Sizes of the Sun and the Earth. The actual sizes of the sun and the earth, and the distance which separates them, are not really of any vital consequence in this connection, and in any case the figures expressed in miles are so large as to be almost incomprehensible. It is, however, quite useful to scale them down to sizes small enough for us to understand. Let us imagine the sun to be the size of a soccer ball. The earth would then be thirty-five yards away and the size of a little silver cachou slightly smaller than the ones used to decorate a birthday cake. You may find it more useful to remember that you can put 100 'earths' across a circle representing the sun.*

Night and Day. The earth travels round the sun along a path known as its *orbit*, making one complete journey in 365¼ days. Since it also spins on its axis once every twenty-four hours, it is obvious that the half of the earth which for the time being is facing the sun will be lit up by the sun's rays, while the other half will be in darkness. Thus, as we spin round with the earth, we pass through daylight half of the time and darkness the other half. But it is not quite true to say 'half of the time', because sometimes the night is longer than the day and sometimes the day is longer than the night, and, if we visit the polar

* On the same scale the moon would be the size of a small pinhead and only 3 inches away from the cachou.

regions at certain times of the year, we shall be in continuous daylight for a few weeks, or, alternatively, in continuous darkness.

This, together with the fact that we have different seasons within the space of a year, is because the earth's axis is not perpendicular to the plane of the ecliptic. Let us suppose that we have a very large, flat surface like an enormous drawing-board, and in the middle of it a soccer ball representing the sun, round which at a radius of 35 yards the silver cachou is travelling in its orbit. The cachou remains in contact with the drawing-board all the time; it does not jump up and down as it passes on its journey, but stays in the same plane or flat surface. This surface is what in the solar system is called the *plane of the ecliptic*, and the earth's axis is inclined to it at an angle of $66\frac{1}{2}°$. It may be that at one time the earth's axis was at right angles to this plane, but the earth appears to be swaying from side to side as it spins (like an ordinary spinning-top when it slows down), and at present the axis is inclined at $66\frac{1}{2}°$. In a few more million years it may become 'upright' again.

Because of this tilt of the axis the northern half of the earth 'leans over' *towards* the sun when the earth is at one side of its orbit (in June) and *away from* it when it has travelled round to the other side (in December). Fig. 173 shows the two positions although it is necessarily very much out of scale.

We can now divide the diagram into two, and show what is happening on the earth in each of the two positions. Before doing so, we must notice one very important point. The sun's rays actually 'radiate' from the sun like the spokes of a wheel,

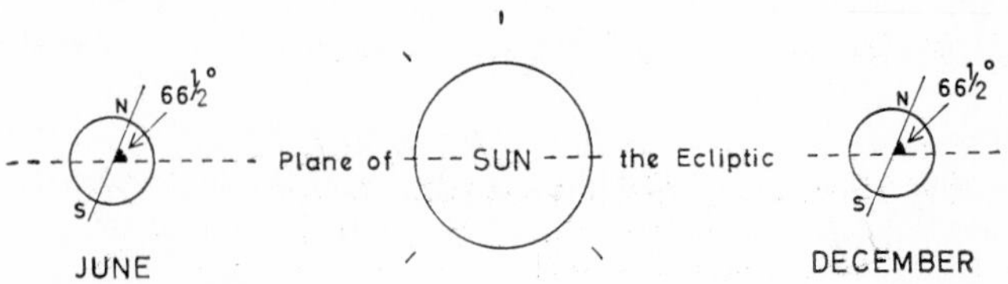

Fig. 173—The tilt of the earth's axis in relation to the plane of the ecliptic.

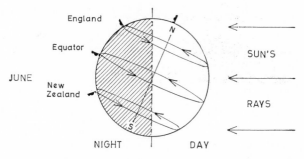

FIG. 174—The comparative lengths of day and night at different latitudes in June.

but the sun is so large and the earth is so small in comparison that for all practical purposes we may consider all the rays which fall on the earth to be parallel to each other. This is the way in which they are shown in the diagrams.

In the diagram for June (Fig. 174), the man on the Equator will experience twelve hours day and twelve hours night as he goes round with the spinning earth. The man north of him (in England, for example) will have a short night and a long day, but the man to the south (say in New Zealand) will have a long night and a short day. The man at the North Pole is in daylight all the time. In fact, in June (i.e. our summer) the period of daylight is longer the nearer we get to the Arctic Circle, and the reverse is true in the southern half of the earth, where the people are in the middle of winter.

With the earth in the December position (Fig. 175), everything is reversed. It is now the Englishman who is getting the long nights and the New Zealander who is getting the long days. But notice that the man on the Equator still has twelve hours day and twelve hours night.

In September, when the earth is half-way between the June position and the December position on its orbit, the tilt of the axis (and remember *the tilt is always 'parallel to itself'*) does not cause any variation in the length of day and night over the

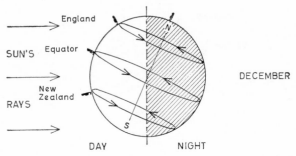

F<small>IG</small>. 175—The comparative lengths of day and night at different latitudes in December.

world (Fig. 176*). The tilt is sideways on to the sun and not towards it, and everyone now has twelve hours day and twelve hours night. The same thing exactly happens again in March, when the earth is half-way from the December to the June position.

So, except on the Equator, the length of day and night varies

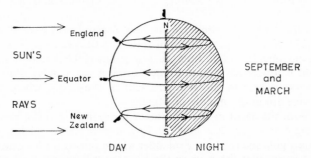

F<small>IG</small>. 176—The length of day and night in September and March.

* Notice that in this position the axis and the division between night and day are represented by the same line (NS). The axis has not disappeared! It is really tilting *away from* you and *towards* you at right angles to the page. Unfortunately it is impossible to draw a three-dimensional diagram on a sheet of paper.

throughout the year. In the British Isles the longest day has about 16½ hours daylight and the shortest day about 7½ hours.

The Seasons. From the September and March diagram (Fig. 176), it will be seen that the sun is then shining directly down on the top of the head of the man on the Equator at midday; or, to put it another way, he sees the sun 'high in the sky'. The

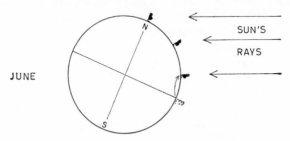

JUNE

SUN'S RAYS

FIG. 177—Insolation at various latitudes in June.

Englishman on the diagram sees the sun half-way up the sky, but the man at the Pole sees only half the sun above the horizon. We know from our own experience that the higher the sun is in the sky, the warmer we are. It is obvious, therefore, that the heating power, or what is known as *insolation*, gets less as we go from (in this case) the Equator to the Poles.*

In the diagram for June (Fig. 177), we see that the position is slightly different. The man on the Equator will have to move a little farther north if he is to have the sun shining directly

* Fig. 179 illustrates the same point in a different way. The heat from a 'bundle' of the sun's rays which strikes the earth near the Pole is dispersed over a larger area than the heat from a similar 'bundle' striking the earth near the Equator. Moreover, near the Poles the rays have to travel a greater distance through the atmosphere than they do near the Equator. Actually, the amount of heat lost in this way is very small indeed.

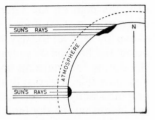

FIG. 179—Insolation.

down on to the top of his head at midday. The Englishman
will see the sun higher in the sky than he did in March or
September; he will therefore be warmer. So too will the man at
the North Pole. When the earth is in this position, people north
of the Equator are having their summer.

In December, when the people north of the Equator are
having winter (Fig. 178), the man on the Equator has to move
farther south to find the warmest part of the earth, the Englishman sees the sun even lower in the sky than he did in March or

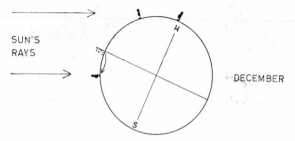

SUN'S
RAYS

DECEMBER

FIG. 178—Insolation at various latitudes in December.

September, and the man at the North Pole cannot see the sun
at all. But in December, the people south of the Equator are
enjoying their summer.

Thus the tilt of the earth's axis is also responsible for causing
the seasons.

The Altitude of the Sun. Since the earth is spinning on its
axis, the man on the Equator in the September and March
diagram (Fig. 176) does not, of course, have the sun directly
above his head all the day, but only at noon. It comes up from
below the horizon at sunrise, climbs higher and higher in the
sky during the morning until it is right overhead at midday,
and then falls lower and lower until it disappears below the
horizon again at sunset. At places away from the Equator, the
sun climbs up the sky until it reaches its highest point for that
time of year, and then falls again (Fig. 180). The nearer you

are to the Equator, the higher the sun gets at midday,* and by measuring the 'height' or altitude of the sun at midday, you can calculate how far you are from the Equator, or, in other words, your latitude. (During the night you will have to work it out from the altitude of the Pole Star—or, if you are in the Southern Hemisphere, the Southern Cross.)

Solstices and Equinoxes. If you look again at the foregoing diagrams, you will see that in the course of the year the sun is directly overhead at noon at the Equator in March, north of the Equator in June, at the Equator again in September, south of the Equator in December, and back to the Equator again in

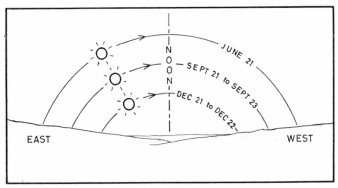

FIG. 180—The sun's path across the sky in England.

March. The overhead sun at noon actually reaches the latitude of 23½° North in June before it turns south again, so this line around the earth is given the special name, the *Tropic of Cancer*, and the date on which it reaches it (usually June 21st) is known as the *June Solstice*.† The line of latitude south of the

* This is universally true at the Equinoxes; it is not, however, necessarily true within the Tropics at other times of the year.

† To refer to the June and December Solstices as the Summer and Winter Solstices respectively is rather misleading. These terms are, however, sometimes used.

Note also that the actual dates of the Solstices and Equinoxes differ slightly, since a year consists of 365¼ days; the quarter-days are put together to make a leap year of 366 days every four years, and so the dates must change.

Equator which the overhead sun at noon reaches in December also has a special name, the *Tropic of Capricorn*, and the date (usually December 22nd) on which the sun reaches it is called the *December Solstice*.* These two dates are our longest and shortest days. March 21st and September 23rd are known as the *Equinoxes*. The Latin from which these words are derived helps us to remember what is happening. 'Equinox' comes from two words meaning 'equal' and 'night', since the day and night are of twelve hours each all over the earth. 'Solstice' means 'the sun stands still' as, presumably, the overhead sun at noon must appear to do, before turning round to go back in the direction from which it has come (Fig. 181).

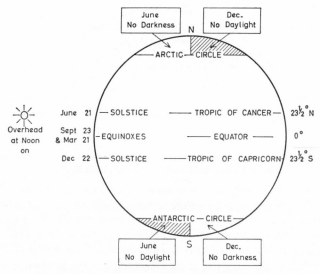

FIG. 181—The movement of the overhead sun at noon.

* See footnote on previous page.

CHAPTER FOURTEEN

Climate

BOTH climate and weather are concerned with the state of the atmosphere and the events that are perpetually taking place in it—the rain, the winds, the clouds, whether it is warm or cold, and so on. But the two words are used in different connections.

When we say 'It rained yesterday morning' or 'I hope it will be fine next Thursday', we are thinking of odd events in the atmosphere which last for only a short time, which do not fit into any particular pattern, and which do not happen with any regularity. Because, for instance, it was cold last Wednesday, there is no reason to suppose that it will be cold next Wednesday. Statements of this kind refer to the *weather*.

When, however, we say 'India has warm, dry winters and hot, wet summers' or 'Russia has warm summers and very cold winters', we are thinking of the state of the atmosphere over much longer periods, and of events which do make up a general pattern which is repeated year after year. Such statements refer to *climate*.

In Chapter 15 we shall discuss the attempts made by the weather-men or *meteorologists* to find out if there are any laws which govern the weather. But first we must try to discover what causes each of the various parts of the world to have its own particular pattern of rain and sunshine, heat and cold, throughout every year, and whether the pattern or climate of any one place is found anywhere else.

There are three main factors by which we can distinguish the climates of the different parts of the world:

   (i) the temperature in summer and winter;
  (ii) the direction of the prevailing winds;
 (iii) the amount of the rainfall, and the time of year in which it falls.

Temperature. In general, one would expect the warmest parts of the world to be those nearest the Equator, where the overhead sun at noon is highest in the sky, and the coldest parts to be those nearest the Poles. If the earth was completely covered by sea or flat land without mountains or valleys, this would be true without exception, but this is not, of course, the case. Some parts of the world are so high that they are much colder than we should expect from their latitude. As we have already seen, Mount Kilimanjaro, almost on the Equator, is snow-capped, and even in England the higher land is noticeably colder than the more low-lying regions.

Moreover, since land heats up and cools down more quickly than sea, land masses are often considerably warmer in summer and colder in winter than areas of sea at the same latitude.

Winds. Just as there is a regular large-scale circulation of the waters of the oceans, so there is a large-scale circulation of the air over the face of the earth. Fig. 182 shows the general movement of the air in the lower part of the atmosphere, in other words, the 'surface' winds. The left-hand side of the diagram shows the full circulation looked at sideways on.

We need not at this stage concern ourselves with what is happening in the upper part of the atmosphere, nor indeed with a full explanation of how the circulation is caused. It is, however, important to notice the following facts:

(i) The circulation is set moving by the hot air rising in the Equatorial regions, causing a *low-pressure* belt—or *convection belt*—all round the Equator. This is the area known to sailors as the *Doldrums*, and in it sailing ships often found themselves becalmed. The air rises in convection currents, but there is very little horizontal movement of air to fill a ship's sails.

(ii) Round about 35° on each side of the Equator, there is a belt of *high pressure*, and very roughly 50° on each side of the Equator there is a belt of *low pressure*. At the Poles the pressure tends to be high.

(iii) Air moving from the high-pressure belts towards the Equator forms the two belts of *Trade Winds*, so called because they blow so steadily and constantly. They were clearly of very

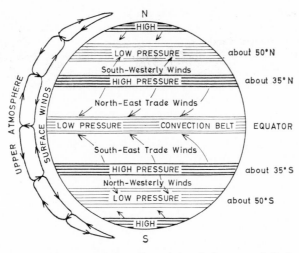

Fig. 182—World pressure belts and the belts of planetary winds. It will help you to remember the direction of the winds if you notice that joined together the arrows make up one of the 'big' brackets sometimes used in Algebra.

great value when overseas trade was carried in sailing ships, but their name is derived from the nautical expression 'to blow trade', meaning 'to blow in a constant direction'.

(iv) Air moving from the high-pressure belts towards the low-pressure belts at 50° N. and 50° S. forms the two belts of *Westerly Winds*. The Westerlies, particularly in the Northern Hemisphere, are by no means as reliable as the Trade Winds, either in direction or force.

(v) These *planetary* winds (so called to distinguish them from less important *local* winds) do not move directly from high pressure to low. Because of the rotation of the earth, they are deflected to left or right of their shortest course from high to low. You should notice that winds in the Northern Hemisphere are deflected to the right, and that winds in the Southern Hemisphere are deflected to the left.

The direction from which the wind blows is of the utmost importance to us in our daily lives since the rainfall to a great extent depends upon it.

Rainfall. The Trade Winds blow towards the Equator from cool regions to comparatively warm regions. They are therefore more and more able to hold the water vapour they contain without 'overflowing', and thus they tend to be dry winds, except on mountainous coasts, where they are forced to rise.

The Westerlies, on the other hand, are moving from warm regions to comparatively cool regions. Since they travel over increasingly cooler parts of the earth's surface, they may well find themselves unable to hold all their water vapour, and the excess will condense as rain. The Westerlies tend therefore to be moist winds. The British Isles lie in the belt of Westerly Winds and we who live there know only too well how often rain comes when the wind is in the west or south-west. Fortunately, the Westerlies are not as reliable as the Trades, otherwise it would rain practically every day.

In the convection belt it does rain almost every day. As soon as the sun has climbed high enough in the sky, the air rises from the heated ground, and there are deluges of thundery rain which cease around nightfall.

THE SWING OF THE WIND BELTS

If the belts of planetary winds remained throughout the year in the positions in which they are shown in Fig. 182, it would be a very simple matter to 'calculate' the climate of any particular part of the earth's surface. The distance from the Equator would tell us a great deal about the temperature, and we should know whether to expect a dry or a wet climate by observing the wind belt in which the selected place was situated.

But the whole system of pressure and wind belts moves slightly northward in summer in the Northern Hemisphere and slightly southward in the winter. It tends to follow the movements of the 'overhead sun at noon' caused by the tilting of the earth's axis, described in the previous chapter. This movement is known as the swing of the wind belts.

Places in the middle of each of the wind belts are not affected by the swing; they remain in one belt throughout the entire year. Others, however, are covered by different wind belts at different times of the year. The various patterns of wet and dry seasons caused by the movement of the wind belts suggest to us one way in which we can classify climates.

The swing does not affect London, for instance. Both summers and winters are wet, since London is affected by the Westerly wind belt throughout the year. But places near the Mediterranean Sea, such as Gibraltar, are in the Trade Wind belt in summer, when the system of belts swings northward, and in the Westerly wind belt in winter, when the system swings southward. The Sahara Desert is covered by the Trades all the year, but Timbuktu has convection rain when the wind belts swing north in the summer and drought from the Trades in winter. Places near the Equator are in the convection belt throughout the year. This is shown in Fig. 183.

The same patterns of wet and dry seasons are repeated in reverse order in the Southern Hemisphere. The entire scheme is shown in the '*Climatic Crossword*' (Fig. 184)—together with the names usually given to the various climates.

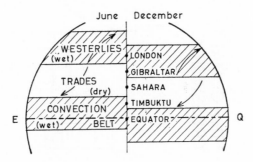

FIG. 183—The effect of the swing of the wind belts on certain places north of the Equator.

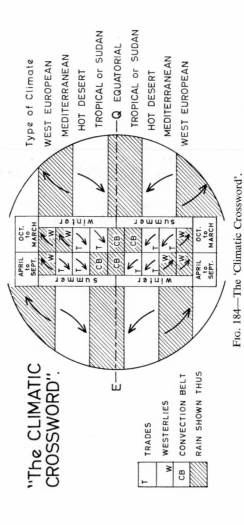

FIG. 184—The 'Climatic Crossword'.

You will see from the climatic map of the world (Fig. 188) at the end of this chapter that the types of climate shown on the 'Crossword' appear only on the western sides of the great land masses. Climates in the central and eastern parts of the land masses have very little to do with the swing of the wind belts and cannot be grouped as easily as those on the western sides. Their underlying causes will, therefore, be dealt with in the more detailed description of world climates which follows.

North and South America display the full range of climatic types based on the wind belts, but Africa does not extend far enough southward to include an area with the West European climate. It is, moreover, important to notice that just as high land and the distribution of land and sea affect the temperature, so do they affect the rainfall.

TYPES OF CLIMATE

1. **West European Climate.** This is the kind of climate which is found not only in the British Isles and the neighbouring areas of western Europe, but also in British Columbia, southern Chile, Tasmania and the South Island of New Zealand. Since these parts of the world are in Westerly wind belts throughout the year, they experience rain at all seasons. On the average they can expect about 30 inches in the year, although some areas have slightly less; and high places like the mountains of western Scotland or exposed places like western Ireland may have considerably more.

It will give you a kind of yard-stick with which to measure the temperatures of other climates if you remember that the British Isles has a July temperature of about 60° F. and a January temperature of about 40° F. We describe the summers, therefore, as 'moderately warm' and the winters as 'mild'. In exceptionally hot summer days the thermometer may reach 90°, and in the course of a bitterly cold winter night there may well be twenty degrees of frost. 'Moderately warm' and 'mild', therefore, probably seem like under-statements. There are, nevertheless, many places with higher summer temperatures than the British Isles, and we must reserve the terms 'warm' and 'hot' for them. Moreover, winter temperatures in Britain really are mild by comparison with the cold experienced in some other regions.

It may also seem to you that 60° is too low a temperature to describe the summer, and that 40° is too high to describe the winter. You must, however, realise that 60° and 40° are the *averages* of all the maximum and minimum temperatures of all the days and nights of all the Julys and Januarys of the last thirty years or so. A batsman's average is 50 if he makes a century in one innings and a 'duck' in the next. That he made a century once does not mean that he will do so in every innings. We compare batsmen—and climates—by their averages, not their outstanding performances.

The climate of the British Isles is often described as 'equable' —that is, with little difference in temperature between summer and winter. The difference between the hottest and the coldest months—the *mean annual range of temperature*—is about 20°, and by comparison with some places this is not very much. In summer the British Isles are kept somewhat cooler than they might otherwise be by the comparatively cool air from off the Atlantic, and in winter warmer than they would be by the fact that the air from off the sea is then comparatively warm.

Monthly figures of temperature and rainfall of two typical places with a West European climate are given below:

London Temp. °F.	J 39	F 40	M 42	A 47	M 53	J 59	J 63	A 62	S 57	O 50	N 44	D 40	24	*Range of Temp.*
Rainfall in inches	1·9	1·7	1·8	1·5	1·8	2·0	2·4	2·2	1·8	2·6	2·4	2·4	24·5	*Total*

Aberdeen Temp. °F.	J 38	F 38	M 40	A 44	M 48	J 54	J 57	A 56	S 53	O 47	N 42	D 39	19	*Range of Temp.*
Rainfall in inches	2·2	2·1	2·4	1·9	2·3	1·7	2·8	2·7	2·2	3·0	3·0	3·2	29·5	*Total*

These figures can be turned into climatic graphs, which are of great help in giving us, as it were, 'pictures' of the climates of particular places. The graph for London is shown in Fig. 185.

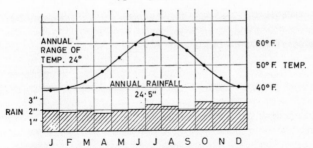

FIG. 185—The climatic graph for London. The method of drawing the graph is as follows:

Draw vertical lines to represent tall rainfall 'jars'. Fill the 'jars' with inches of rainfall to the appropriate depth, then place a dot above the *centre* of each jar to represent the temperature for the month, and draw a line through the dots.

If you are using an ordinary school exercise book, you will probably find it most convenient to make the 'jars' ¼ inch wide and to let the space between any two lines in the book represent 2 inches of rainfall and 10 degrees of temperature.

You should draw for yourself graphs for Aberdeen and the other places which will be mentioned later.

2. **Mediterranean Climate.** The Mediterranean climate is that of the south of Spain, the Riviera coast of France, of northern California and Cape Town, and of any other regions where the dry Trade Winds blow in summer and the rain-bearing Westerlies in winter. The hot, dry summers make such regions very popular with holiday-makers, but present difficulties to the farmers, faced with the problem of watering their crops (see Fig. 186).

Gibraltar	J	F	M	A	M	J	J	A	S	O	N	D		
Temp. °F.	55	56	57	61	65	70	73	75	72	67	60	56	20	Range of Temp.
Rainfall in inches		5·1	4·2	4·8	2·7	1·7	·5	—	·1	1·4	3·3	6·4	5·5	35·7	Total

San Francisco	J	F	M	A	M	J	J	A	S	O	N	D		
Temp. °F.	49	51	53	54	56	57	57	58	60	59	56	51	11	Range of Temp.
Rainfall in inches		4·8	3·6	3·1	1·0	·7	·1	—	—	·3	1·0	2·4	4·6	21·6	Total

FIG. 186—A river bed near Xilokastron in southern Greece in summer. This scene is typical of many rivers in Mediterranean regions during the dry summer months. In Ancient Greece river beds such as this were frequently used as roads! Notice the amount of eroded material which has been temporarily deposited.

3. **Hot Desert Climate.** In the Hot Desert climate, where the Trade Winds blow all the year round, the total rainfall may amount to only a few inches, and usually comes at infrequent intervals in the form of heavy thunder-showers. The driest part of the world is the Atacama Desert in South America, and there are places in the Great Australian Desert where there has sometimes been no rain for years.

Owing to the clear skies, it is often much hotter at midday than on the Equator, but at night in any of the great deserts you would probably find it distinctly chilly.

Aden	J	F	M	A	M	J	J	A	S	O	N	D		Range
Temp. °F.	76	77	79	83	87	89	88	87	88	84	80	77	13	of Temp.
Rainfall in inches	·3	·2	·5	·2	·1	·1	—	·1	·1	·1	·1	·1	1·9	Total

Antofagasta	J	F	M	A	M	J	J	A	S	O	N	D		Range
Temp. °F.	72	70	70	67	64	63	62	60	61	62	64	68	12	*of Temp.*
Rainfall in inches					*practically nil*								—	*Total*

N.B.—*Since Antofagasta is in the Southern Hemisphere the highest temperature is in January.*

4. **Tropical or Sudan Climate.** The Tropical or Sudan climate has summer rain from the convection belt and winter drought from the Trades. It is, therefore, in this respect opposite to the Mediterranean climate. Summers are almost as hot as in the Equatorial climate, and winters very warm.

Kingston (Jamaica)	J	F	M	A	M	J	J	A	S	O	N	D		Range
Temp. °F.	77	77	77	78	80	81	82	82	82	81	79	78	5	*of Temp.*
Rainfall in inches	1·0	·6	1·0	1·2	4·3	4·1	1·7	3·7	4·1	7·5	3·1	1·0	33·3	*Total*

Bulawayo	J	F	M	A	M	J	J	A	S	O	N	D		Range
Temp. °F.	71	70	69	66	61	58	57	61	67	71	72	72	15	*of Temp.*
Rainfall in inches	5·5	4·8	4·5	·8	·6	—	—	—	·3	·6	3·1	4·9	25·1	*Total*

(*Southern Hemisphere*)

5. **Equatorial Climate.** We cannot very well talk about 'summer' and 'winter' in connection with places very close to the Equator. But this does not matter very much, since it is hot all the year round, and it rains on practically every day of the year, usually in the afternoon, after the sun has climbed high enough in the sky to set up convection currents in the air.

Singapore	J	F	M	A	M	J	J	A	S	O	N	D		Range
Temp. °F.	80	80	81	82	82	81	81	81	81	81	81	80	2	*of Temp.*
Rainfall in inches	9·9	6·6	7·4	7·6	6·7	6·8	6·8	7·9	6·8	8·1	9·9	10·6	95·1	*Total*

New Antwerp (Congo)	J	F	M	A	M	J	J	A	S	O	N	D		Range
Temp. °F.	79	80	79	78	79	78	77	76	77	77	78	78	4	*of Temp*
Rainfall in inches	4·1	3·5	4·1	5·6	6·2	6·1	6·3	6·3	6·3	6·6	2·6	9·3	67	*Total*

6. **Tropical Monsoon Climate.** In the south-east of the great land mass of Asia, in such countries as India and China, the

Climate

climate has very little to do with the planetary wind belts. It is almost entirely controlled by the enormous size of the continent. In winter the centre of Asia becomes very cold indeed. At one place (Verkhoyansk) the average temperature in January is — 58° F.! This is due to the fact that it is so far away from the warming influence of the sea. The pressure consequently becomes very high, and winds blow outward to warmer parts of the earth's surface to the south and east. But in summer the land heats up very rapidly, a powerful centre of low pressure forms to the north of India, and air from off the cooler waters of the Indian Ocean and the China Sea is drawn inwards to the land (Fig. 187). These winds are, in effect, a land breeze and a sea breeze on a vast scale.

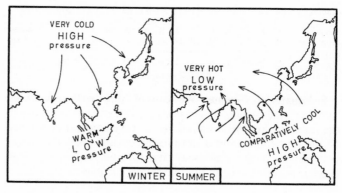

FIG. 187—The relation of monsoon winds to high and low pressure over Asia.

The outblowing air in winter is clearly unlikely to contain very much water vapour. The winters in South-East Asia (in which temperatures may well be 15° above those of our summer) are therefore dry. But towards the end of May moisture-laden air, drawn into the low-pressure area, is forced to rise as it meets the land, and for the next three or four months very heavy monsoon rainfall is experienced.

Various other parts of the world are affected by the drawing inward of air from the sea to an overheated land mass, but in few of them is the monsoon so spectacular as it is in South-East Asia.

Bombay	J	F	M	A	M	J	J	A	S	O	N	D		
Temp. °F.	76	76	80	83	86	84	81	81	81	82	81	77	10	*Range of Temp.*
Rainfall in inches	·1	·1	—	—	·7	19·9	24·0	14·5	10·6	1·9	·4	—	72·2	*Total*

Hong Kong	J	F	M	A	M	J	J	A	S	O	N	D		
Temp. °F.	60	59	63	70	77	81	82	82	81	76	69	63	23	*Range of Temp.*
Rainfall in inches	1·3	1·8	2·7	5·3	12·0	15·8	14·0	14·6	9·7	5·1	1·7	1·1	85·1	*Total*

7. **Continental Climate.** The Continental climate of the centre of Asia and North America is also caused by the enormous size of these land masses. It is not found in the Southern Hemisphere, since there are no land masses large enough or wide enough in high latitudes. The great distance from the sea causes the centre of Asia and the centre of North America to become extremely cold in winter, although in summer the temperature is about the same as in the British Isles. Such regions are, therefore, particularly noteworthy for their great mean annual range of temperature. The precipitation* is not very heavy. By the time the winds have reached these inland areas they have already deposited most of their excess water vapour.

As we move outwards from the centres of the land masses, the annual range becomes less, and the Continental climate merges into the West European and Laurentian climates.

Verkhoyansk	J	F	M	A	M	J	J	A	S	O	N	D		
Temp. °F.	−58	−48	−24	9	36	56	60	52	36	6	−34	−51	118	*Range of Temp.*
Rainfall in inches	·2	·1	·1	·2	·3	·9	1·0	1·0	·5	·4	·3	·1	5·1	*Total*

Moscow	J	F	M	A	M	J	J	A	S	O	N	D		
Temp. °F.	12	15	24	38	53	62	66	63	52	40	28	17	54	*Range of Temp.*
Rainfall in inches	1·1	·9	1·2	1·5	1·9	2·0	2·8	2·9	2·2	1·4	1·6	1·5	21	*Total*

* *Precipitation*—a word used to include all the forms in which water may fall from the atmosphere—snow, sleet, hail, etc., as well as rain.

Winnipeg Temp. °F.	J	F	M	A	M	J	J	A	S	O	N	D		Range of Temp.
	−4	0	15	38	52	62	66	64	54	41	21	6	70	
Rainfall in inches	·9	·7	1·2	1·4	2·0	3·1	3·1	2·2	2·2	1·4	1·1	·9	20·2	Total

8. **Laurentian Climate.** The Laurentian climate borders the Continental climate on its eastern side. It is really very much like the West European climate, except that its range of temperature is somewhat greater. You will probably have gathered from films and newspaper articles of events in New York that the only real difference lies in the fact that New York experiences rather more heat-waves in summer and blizzards in winter than places in the British Isles.

New York Temp. °F.	J	F	M	A	M	J	J	A	S	O	N	D		Range of Temp.
	31	31	38	48	59	68	73	72	66	56	44	34	42	
Rainfall in inches	3·3	3·3	3·4	3·3	3·5	3·5	4·1	4·3	3·4	3·4	3·3	3·3	42·1	Total

9. **Warm Temperate East Coast Climate.** The Warm Temperate East Coast climate, although sometimes known as the 'Gulf' or 'China' type, is usually given its name in full. It is the climate in which the Test Matches at Sydney are played, and the climate in which the tired business-man from New York relaxes on the holiday beaches of Miami and Palm Beach in Florida.

This too is somewhat similar to the West European climate, but about 12° warmer both in summer and winter. Rain falls at all times of the year, with slightly more in summer than in winter. It is, however, a particularly sunny climate. There are very few periods of prolonged 'drizzle'; the rain comes in heavy showers which are soon over.

Sydney Temp. °F.	J	F	M	A	M	J	J	A	S	O	N	D		Range of Temp.
	72	71	69	65	59	55	53	55	59	64	67	70	19	
Rainfall in inches	3·7	4·3	4·8	5·6	5·1	4·8	4·8	3·0	2·9	3·2	2·8	2·9	47·9	Total

10. **Cold Desert Climate.** The high plateau regions of the Rocky Mountains of North America and the centre of Asia have a great range of temperature and very little rain. These

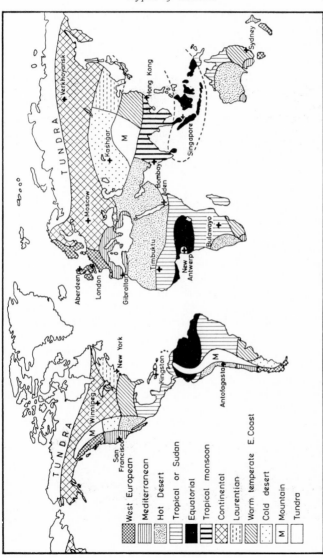

Fig. 188—Climatic map of the world (simplified).

cold deserts are really a special section of the areas with Continental climate.

Kashgar	J	F	M	A	M	J	J	A	S	O	N	D		Range
Temp. °F.	22	34	47	61	70	77	80	76	69	56	40	26	58	of Temp.
Rainfall in inches	·3	—	·2	·2	·8	·4	·3	·7	·3	—	—	·2	3·4	Total

N.B.—*Kashgar is 4,255 feet above sea-level.*

11. **Tundra Climate.** The Arctic and Antarctic regions have long, very cold winters and very brief summers. In the summer the surface of the ground may thaw out in swampy patches, but throughout most of the year there is nothing to break the vast expanse of snow and ice.

12. **Mountain Climates.** In very high fold mountains, such as the Andes and Himalayas, the climate depends more upon height above sea-level than upon anything else. It is, therefore, impossible to fit such mountain areas into any one particular climatic division.

The Climatic Map of the World. In using the climatic map of the world (Fig. 188), you should bear two points in mind.

(i) It is a *simplified* climatic map. Climate is a large and complicated subject, and you will come across more detailed maps in other text-books, but for the time being it is sufficient for you to grasp the main essentials.

(ii) Neighbouring climates merge gradually into one another. You must not imagine that the line dividing, for example, the West European climate from the Mediterranean climate is like a fence with winter rainfall and summer drought on one side and rain all the year on the other!

CHAPTER FIFTEEN

Weather

APART from being a very useful subject with which to bridge an awkward gap in conversation, the weather has always been a matter of great interest to people who lead an outdoor life or who live in parts of the world where conditions change rapidly from day to day. This is so true of the British Isles that somebody once said that Britain has no climate, it only has weather!

We have all at one time or another heard quoted the old rhyme:

> 'Red sky at night, shepherd's delight;
> Red sky in the morning, shepherd's warning.'

Until about a hundred years ago, when scientific weather forecasting began, weather knowledge was almost entirely confined to little rhymes of this kind. Shepherds or fishermen noticed that a red sky at sunset was usually followed by a fine day, or that a clear moon was followed by a frost and turned their observations into rhymes to help them remember. There are literally thousands of such rhymes. In 1898 a man called Richard Inwards published a 200-page book full of them! None of the people who invented or used these little tags of weather-lore knew the reasons behind them. The one quoted above does, as a matter of fact, contain a certain amount of truth, but many of them have since been found to be quite untrue.

Scientific weather study on modern lines was made possible about the middle of the nineteenth century by the invention of the electric telegraph. Visitors to the Great Exhibition in Hyde Park in 1851 could buy for a penny a chart showing the weather existing at various places in the British Isles. It was merely a novelty and no attempt was made to forecast the weather. The map simply gave the barometric pressure, an arrow showing the direction of the wind, and information about whether it was fine, cloudy or raining. It would, of course, have been impossible to gather all these facts together quickly enough but for the invention of the telegraph. Until 1900 a Daily Weather Report was issued, but this was little more than a storm-warning service for seamen.

With the invention in 1898 of wireless communication, it became possible to collect information about weather conditions from very much farther afield. The information which came in from ships at sea was particularly useful. There was already more than a suspicion that the weather experienced in the British Isles came eastwards across the Atlantic. In fact, this idea of the 'travel of weather' was to a large extent confirmed now that it had become possible to draw 'pressure pictures' by means of isobars (see Fig. 158, p. 162), showing the variations of pressure from day to day over the Atlantic and the British Isles. Maps giving such information are called *synoptic charts*. The word 'synoptic' is derived from Greek and means 'seen together at the same time'.

DEPRESSIONS AND ANTICYCLONES

It was soon discovered that the isobars very often tended to form into closed circles or ovals. Some of these circles had low pressure in the centre and higher pressure on the outside, while some (usually larger than the others) had high pressure in the centre and low pressure on the outside. The circles of low pressure were originally called cyclones, but they are now usually termed *depressions*; and the circles of high pressure were, and still are, called *anticyclones*. Fig. 189 shows the kind of 'pressure picture' which was revealed by drawing in the isobars.

The two facts which proved so very interesting were as follows:

  (i) Whereas anticyclones tend to form, remain stationary for a time, and then fade out, depressions tend to move

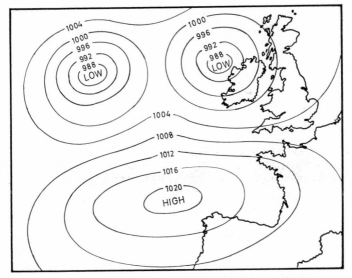

Fig. 189—A typical pressure situation over the Atlantic area.

along reasonably well-defined tracks from west to east at
about 30 or 40 miles per hour.

(ii) Depressions and anticyclones bring with them their own
particular kinds of weather.

Books published in the early years of this century show diagrams of a depression similar to the one in Fig. 190. The arrows
inside the depression showed the direction of the winds, and
there were descriptions of the kind of weather in each section.
If, therefore, you could predict the position of the depression
twenty-four hours hence, you could advise the areas over
which it was likely to travel what kind of weather to expect.
Unfortunately, the depressions did not always turn out 'according to plan', nor could they always be relied on to keep
moving at the same speed or in the expected direction.
Although some progress had been made, the forecasts were
still very frequently inaccurate.

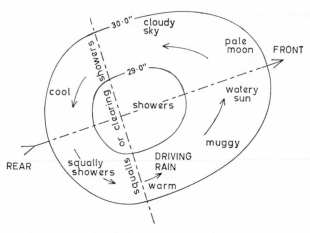

FIG. 190—Weather in a depression (after Abercrombie).

The anticyclones proved to be more reliable. Once an anticyclone has established itself, it is reasonably certain to bring a spell of cold, frosty nights and sunny days in winter, or a warm dry spell in summer, in some cases amounting to a 'heatwave'. In both cases, the weather conditions are due to the absence of strong winds and the cloudless skies which are characteristic of an area of high pressure, where the air is moving gently downwards.

The Polar Front Theory. So far no one had put forward a scientific explanation of what happens to the air within the centres of low pressure to cause the type of weather experienced. But about the time of the First World War, two Norwegians, father and son, named Bjerknes, put forward their Polar Front Theory. They suggested that depressions were formed along the line of the *polar front*—i.e. where the cold, north-easterly airstream blowing from the North Pole meets the warm, south-westerly airstream from the Tropics (Fig. 191). Since, they said, the two airstreams are moving alongside each other but in opposite directions, it was likely that 'dents' would arise in the

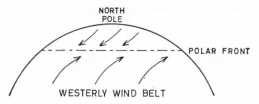

Fɪɢ. 191—The polar front.

front where some of the warm tropical air got caught up in the cold polar air (Fig. 192).

Cold air is denser and heavier than warm air, and pushes its way, therefore, under the warm air, particularly when it has swung round to the position shown in stage 4. By this time there are two definite 'sides' to the original 'dent', which is shown on the synoptic chart by the symbols indicated in Fig. 193.

The part of the polar front marked *A* is called the *cold front*, and is shown by a line of 'spikes' (meaning 'this is the front of the mass of cold air moving in the direction in which the "spikes" are pointing'), and the part of the polar front marked *B* is called the *warm front*, and is shown by a line of 'lumps' (meaning 'this is the front of the mass of warm air moving in the direction in which the "lumps" are pointing'). As the depression grows older, the cold front moves closer to the warm front, pushing the warm air upwards. Eventually, the cold front catches up with the warm front in what is called the *occlusion*,* the depression disappears, and the 'dent' in the polar front is smoothed out.

This explanation of the inner working of a depression fits in extremely well with the observed weather conditions. The *warm sector* between the two fronts, where the warm air is being forced upwards, is clearly the area most likely to produce rain, the direction of the winds in the various parts of the depression are explained, and the squally, cooler weather which so often follows a spell of rain is shown to be due to the passing of the cold front.

* From the Latin word meaning 'to close'.

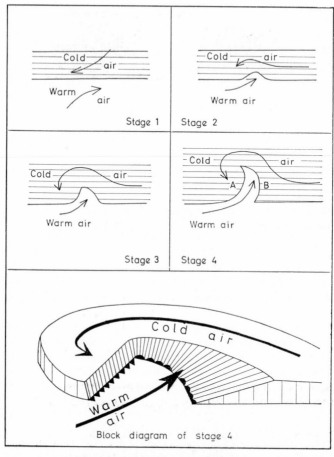

Fig. 192—The growth of a depression.

The Bjerknes' explanation of the formation of depressions is in the main still accepted, but very few depressions run true to type, and in any case many of them are almost completely

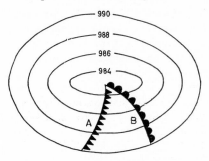

FIG. 193—The symbols used to indicate the cold front (*A*) and the warm front (*B*).

occluded by the time they reach the British Isles. Moreover, owing to the increasing use of aircraft making meteorological flights and of instruments sent up into the atmosphere attached to balloons, we can gather many more detailed observations of temperature and humidity than was formerly possible, particularly of the upper air a mile or more above ground. It has, as a result, been realised that there is much more to the problem than a single polar front where cold and warm air move side by side.

Air Masses. There seem to be four main types of air mass which affect the British Isles at various times and which are derived from high-pressure areas in polar or tropical regions.

   (i) *Polar Maritime Air*, which has come from off the seas in high latitudes, and is cold and moist.
  (ii) *Polar Continental Air*, from polar land masses. This is cold and dry.
 (iii) *Tropical Maritime Air*, from tropical sea areas. This is warm and moist.
 (iv) *Tropical Continental Air*, from tropical land areas. This is warm and dry.

The British Isles and the northern Atlantic Ocean are a kind of battleground, where the air masses fight for supremacy.

Meteorological experts in the Central Forecasting Office forecast the weather which is likely to result from the meeting of these air masses, mainly on the basis of their experience of what happened the last time a similar situation occurred.

It would, of course, be a great help to forecasters if we could find out by studying the conditions in the places where these air masses come from what starts them moving. It is for this reason that meteorological stations have been set up in the lonely regions near the North Pole.

THE DAILY WEATHER FORECAST

The various readings of temperature, pressure, humidity, wind direction and so on, broadcast by ships at sea and by 'met. stations' at certain times of the day, are collected by teleprinter at the Central Forecasting Office at Bracknell (formerly at Dunstable) and plotted on special maps by qualified assistants. The skilled forecaster then examines the situation, joins up the places with the same pressure to form the isobars, and adds the fronts where he thinks two masses of air with different characteristics meet each other. He then forecasts the weather to be expected in each of the areas into which the British Isles and the surrounding seas are divided.

The official weather map summarising all this information is compiled in a kind of meteorological 'shorthand'. It has to be, otherwise there would not be enough room around each of the little circles indicating a recording station to give a full description of the existing weather conditions. It would take far too long to give a detailed account of all the various symbols which are used in connection with the official weather map. The following brief explanation must, therefore, suffice.

The Beaufort Scale. Meteorological 'shorthand' really began in 1806, when a certain Admiral Beaufort suggested that a scale of numbers from 0 to 12 could be used to indicate the varying amounts of sail that a man-of-war could carry in winds of different speeds. 'Calm' was indicated by the figure 0 and a 'Hurricane' of over 75 m.p.h. was allotted the figure 12. In between came 'Light Breeze' at No. 3, 'Moderate Gale' at No. 7, and so on. A landlubber's version of the original Beaufort Scale was subsequently brought out, in which the speed of the wind was related to the effects produced in trees, etc. This is shown on p. 216. Arrows are used on the weather map itself, and are attached to the circles which represent the recording stations so as to show the direction of the wind.* The wind's speed is shown by the number of feathers on the arrow.

Another form of meteorological 'shorthand' due originally to Admiral Beaufort is the use of letters of the alphabet to describe weather conditions—*b* for blue sky, *c* for cloudy, *r* for rain, and so on. These abbreviations are used both by the meteorologist in jotting down his observations and by the compiler of the actual weather map.† The full scale of Beaufort letters is shown on p. 217, together with the International Symbols which are also used for some of them.

There are one or two very helpful refinements which you should notice:

(i) Where the particular feature described is very intense, a capital letter is used, e.g. R means 'heavy rain'.

(ii) Where it is continuous, the letter is repeated, e.g. rr means 'continuous rain', RR means 'continuous heavy rain'.

(iii) Where it is only slight, the suffix $_0$ is used, e.g. r_0 means 'slight rain'.

Reproductions of parts of the old and the new style daily weather maps are shown in Figs. 194 and 195. You can, if you wish, arrange for the map to be posted to you daily for little more than the cost of the postage.‡ On each issue there is a full explanation of the symbols, and you would find it quite

---

* They should be visualised as darts which are flying along in the same direction as the wind.

† They are no longer shown on the *published* map.

‡ Or get your school to order it for the Geography Room or the School Notice Board.

THE BEAUFORT WIND SCALE

Beaufort No.	Wind	Arrow	Speed m.p.h.	Commonly observed effects of corresponding winds
0	Calm	⊙	0	Calm, smoke rises vertically.
1	Light air		2	Direction of wind shown by smoke drift, but not by wind vanes.
2	Light breeze		5	Wind felt on face; leaves rustle; ordinary vane moved by wind.
3	Gentle breeze		10	Leaves and small twigs in constant motion; wind extends light flag.
4	Moderate breeze		15	Raises dust and loose paper; small branches are moved.
5	Fresh breeze		21	Small trees in leaf begin to sway; crested wavelets form on inland waters.
6	Strong breeze		28	Large branches in motion; whistling heard in telegraph wires; umbrellas used with difficulty.
7	Moderate gale		35	Whole trees in motion; inconvenience felt when walking against wind.
8	Fresh gale		42	Breaks twigs off trees; generally impedes progress.
9	Strong gale		50	Slight structural damage occurs (chimney pots and slates removed).
10	Whole gale		59	Seldom experienced inland; trees uprooted; considerable structural damage occurs.
11	Storm		69	Very rarely experienced; accompanied by widespread damage.
12	Hurricane		above 75	....

THE BEAUFORT LETTERS AND INTERNATIONAL SYMBOLS

(1) *Appearance of Sky*

b		Blue sky whether with clear or hazy atmosphere.
c		Cloudy, i.e. detached opening clouds.
o		Overcast, i.e. the whole sky covered with one impervious cloud.
g		Gale.
u		Ugly, threatening sky.

(2) *Wind*

q	Squalls.
KQ	Line squall.

(3) *Precipitation*

r	●	Rain.
p	▽	Passing showers.
d	﹐	Drizzle.
s	✳	Snow.
rs	✶	Sleet.
h	▲	Hail.

(4) *Electrical Phenomena*

t		Thunder.
l	⦚	Distant lightning.
tl	⏃	Thunderstorm.

(5) *Atmospheric Obscurity and Water Vapour*

f	≡	Fog ⎫
fe		Wet fog ⎬ Range of visibility less than 1,100 yards.
z	∞	Haze, range of visibility 1,100 yards or more, but less than 2,200 yards.
m	=	Mist, range of visibility 1,100 yards or more, but less than 2,200 yards.
v	Ô	Unusual visibility of distant objects.
e		Wet air, without rain falling.
y		Dry air.

(6) *Ground Phenomena*

w	⌓	Dew.
x	⊔	Hoar-frost.

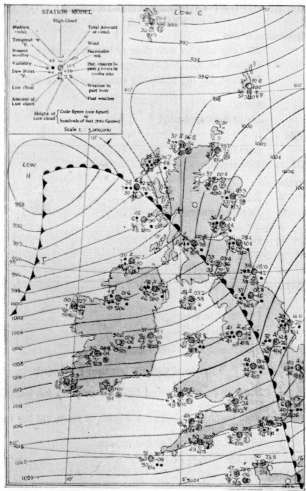

Reproduced by permission of the Director, Meteorological Office and the Controller of H.M. Stationery Office.

FIG. 194—Part of the daily weather report for 7 Feb. 1948.

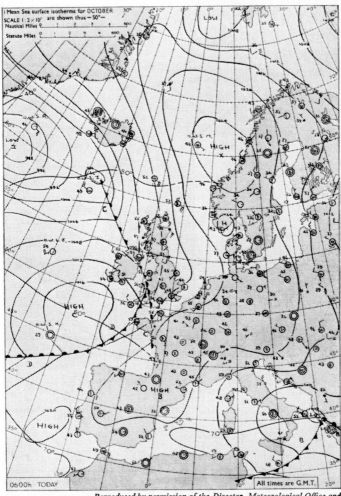

Reproduced by permission of the Director, Meteorological Office and the Controller of H.M. Stationery Office.

FIG. 195—Part of the daily weather report for 12 Oct. 1959.

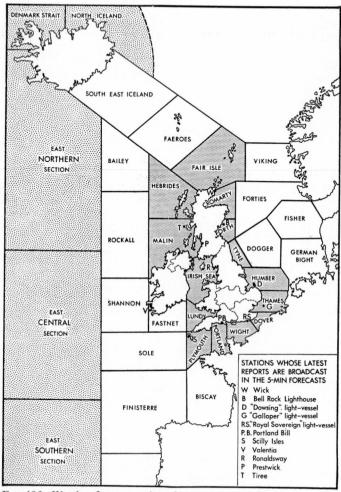

Fig. 196—Weather forecast regions for sea areas. The tinted areas surrounding the British Isles are those in which 'visual gale warnings' are displayed by coastal stations. When a gale is expected, a cone is hoisted to the top of a mast, with its point upwards to indicate a northerly gale and with its point downwards for a southerly gale. By night a triangle of lights is used in place of a cone.

interesting to watch the pressure pattern gradually changing from day to day, and the movements of the depressions and the fronts. You might even try a little forecasting for yourself! Nowadays so many people take an interest not only in the actual forecast, but also in the why and wherefore that lie behind it, that most newspapers include a simplified form of the official weather map; and one is also provided each evening on the television programmes.

Fig. 196 shows the forecast regions for sea areas referred to in the B.B.C. Shipping Forecast.

CHAPTER SIXTEEN

Vegetation

NATURAL VEGETATION REGIONS

FOR plants of any kind to grow, the surface rock must, of course, have been sufficiently broken down by weathering to provide a layer of soil in which they can take root. Apart from this (which will be considered in the next chapter), all plants require three things for their growth—heat, light and moisture. Only in the polar regions is the light insufficient, and even here a crop of bright little flowers may, in the brief period of continuous sunlight, spring up and wither, all within the space of a few weeks. It is, therefore, chiefly the temperature and the amount of rainfall which decide the type of natural vegetation. If you compare the map of the world showing vegetation (Fig. 197) with the climatic map (Fig. 188, p. 205), you will see how closely the divisions coincide.

1. **The Equatorial Forest Regions.** In the regions of Equatorial climate, where there is great heat and heavy rainfall throughout the year, the land is covered with dense forest. A bewildering variety of tall, slender trees, with most of their branches near the top, compete with each other for existence. The branches mat together so closely that they almost shade the ground from the sun, and create what has been described as 'a green twilight' beneath. The forests are often called 'evergreen', but the trees, like oaks and elms in the British Isles, do in fact cast off their leaves. But whereas the deciduous trees of temperate latitudes all shed their leaves together in the autumn, different trees in the Equatorial Forests—indeed different parts of the same tree—may be shedding their leaves at different times of the year.

Besides the trees themselves, a multitude of other plants grow

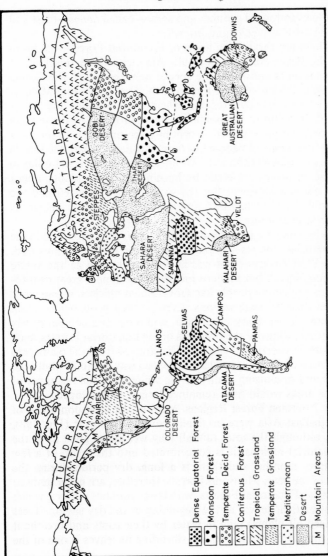

Fig. 197—Natural vegetation map of the world.

Dense Equatorial Forest
Monsoon Forest
Temperate Decid. Forest
Coniferous Forest
Tropical Grassland
Temperate Grassland
Mediterranean
Desert
M Mountain Areas

in the waterlogged ground, and some—called *lianas*—twist and twine around trunks and branches.

There are three main areas of Equatorial Forest—the basin of the River Amazon in South America, where this kind of vegetation is known by the special name of *selvas*, the Congo Basin in Africa, and the region of the East Indies and Malaya. They are obviously regions where Nature holds the upper hand. It is almost impossible to travel through the dense mass of trees and undergrowth except by river, and some of the most primitive kinds of people live here, satisfied to roam the forests in search of fruits and nuts. Where the vegetation is not quite so dense, clearings are made by burning down the plants, and a few crops are grown. But the soil is soon exhausted and the people move on to make another clearing. This is known as *shifting agriculture*.

White men find it extremely difficult to remain for long in the Equatorial Forests without their health becoming impaired. The West African coast was at one time known as 'the White Man's Grave', but modern medicine has done a great deal towards protecting people like Government officials, whose work takes them to such regions. Even so they probably have six months 'leave' every other year, and retire at a comparatively early age. Many of the products of the Equatorial Forests, such as rubber, cacao, and various oils extracted from the plants, are essential to us in our modern European way of life. Without the skill and organising ability of the white man, the resources of these areas would have remained largely undeveloped.

2. **Monsoon Forest Regions.** Most of the monsoon areas of South-East Asia were originally covered by forest (Fig. 198), but, although the total rainfall may well be as great as in the Equatorial regions, it is concentrated into the space of a few summer months, and there is a long, dry period during the rest of the year. Monsoon Forests, therefore, are never quite so dense as Equatorial Forests, with fewer varieties of trees, which all shed their leaves at the beginning of the dry season. Trees (indeed all plants) take in water by their roots and breathe it out mainly from their leaves. Shedding its leaves is one of the

Fig. 198—Monsoon Forests in Thailand.

ways in which a tree adjusts itself in order to slow down the process of 'breathing out' or *transpiration*. By means of this self-imposed rationing, it is able to survive when the soil has dried out.

Monsoon areas are very favourable to man; indeed, they include nearly half the entire population of the world. The forests can be cleared fairly easily and a wide variety of crops is grown. Quite apart from rice, which forms a principal item of diet of the native peoples, such crops as tea, coffee, cotton and sugar, which are nowadays essential to the inhabitants of temperate lands, are also grown.

Some of the areas classed on the map as Monsoon Forest are so far removed from the sea that the sudden summer rains are not so plentiful as in the coastal areas. In such regions the

Hunting Aerosurveys, Ltd.

FIG. 199—Savanna country in East Africa.

trees are much more widely spaced, and in between there is long tropical grass, similar to that described below in Section 3.

3. **Tropical Grassland Regions.** The Tropical Grasslands (Fig. 199) are found in regions of Sudan climate. In some ways 'grassland' is a misleading word to use, since we are apt to think of something rather like the grass of an English meadow. Moreover, Tropical Grasslands are often described as *parkland*, but they are very different from an English 'park'. During the summer rains caused by convection, enormous blades of 'grass' grow rapidly to heights of 6, 10 and even 15 feet. Later in the year, in the period of drought which comes with the Trade Winds, they are scorched by the sun and turn brown.

In addition to the grass, there are some scattered trees. It must be remembered that these Tropical Grassland or *savanna* regions occur between the Equatorial Forests and the Hot Deserts; the number of trees and the height of the grass, therefore, grows less as we pass from one extreme to the other. In one part of South America the Tropical Grasslands are known as *llanos* and in another as *campos*.

The native peoples of the savannas vary in the stage of civilisation they have reached. The Masai people of Kenya are not very advanced; they hunt lions and keep a few cattle from which they drink not only the milk, but also the blood! But the Hausas of Northern Nigeria are much more cultured. They have learnt how to keep herds of cattle, they grow a variety of useful crops and are skilful weavers of cotton and workers in earthenware, leather and iron.

For the white man there are wide possibilities in the Tropical Grasslands. Cotton, coffee, and tropical fruits like pineapples and bananas can be grown, and it should be possible to raise large herds of beef cattle. Unfortunately, the savannas are the home of various insects, such as the tsetse fly, the carrier of 'sleeping sickness', which are dangerous to man and beast alike. Swarms of locusts (which actually breed in the desert) are apt to descend upon the crops. Nowadays, however, rapid progress is being made in mastering such problems as these, and the better organised parts of the Tropical Grasslands are gradually beginning to play a more important part in world affairs.

4. **The Hot Deserts.** In the Hot Deserts, situated in the Trade Wind belt all the year round, the annual rainfall is less than 10 inches, and much of this is evaporated before it can sink into the ground. It may seem surprising, therefore, that under such conditions plants exist at all. Certain kinds of plants have, however, learnt how to survive. Some by growing specially long roots manage to find water below the surface; some by developing waxy, leathery skins prevent transpiration; and some hoard up their little stores of water in bulbs. But even so, such plants have every appearance of being completely dead, until a sudden and long-awaited thunder-shower brings them to life again.

Desert soils are not necessarily infertile; where the water-table comes close to the surface, an 'island' of rich vegetation (or *oasis*) may occur. Many of us derive our impressions of an oasis from early recollections of biblical pictures depicting a tiny pool of water, a palm tree, a bearded old man and a couple of sheep. But many of the more important oases in the Sahara cover almost as much ground as a large English town, and at the time of a market or 'fair' are thronged with people. There are Arab peoples who live permanently in such oases cultivating their crops of melons, figs, dates, and even wheat and barley, and tending their flocks of sheep and goats.

Some people, for example the Bedouin Arabs of North Africa, manage to wrest a living from the scanty vegetation of the *scrublands* on the edges of deserts by following their sheep, goats and camels from pasture to pasture. Such wandering peoples (or *nomads*) as the Bedouins often have a reputation for plundering their neighbours in more highly favoured regions.

If water could be brought to deserts such as the Sahara, there are good reasons for supposing that they would make a very welcome addition to the world's food-producing areas. As far as can be seen at present, the water would have to come from deep wells, and vast and expensive irrigation works would have to be built. In the case of the Thar Desert, the River Indus is, fortunately, available for this purpose, and the waters of the river are controlled by the great dam at Sukkur and distributed by channels over the thirsty land. In many areas, however, there are no conveniently situated rivers. In time it may be possible to create rainfall by releasing chemical substances from aircraft into the clouds. Some progress has already been made in Australia and America by such methods.

5. **'Mediterranean' Regions.** In 'Mediterranean' regions plants are faced by very much the same problem that confronts them in the deserts—how to survive without water. But in this case the drought lasts for only half the year, and since temperatures are high enough during the rainy period of winter for growth to go on, there is no real lack of vegetation. Sufficient

trees were at one time found to justify many parts of the 'Mediterranean' areas being classed as 'woodland', but most of the larger trees have now been cut down. There are now many contrasting types of scenery and vegetation from fertile, well-cultivated plains to barren mountain sides.

Most of the plants are evergreens, and all of them have learnt how to keep alive during the summer with very little water. Some, like the vine, have roots long enough to reach down to the saturated layers well below the surface; others, like the laurel, have leaves covered with a waxy substance which prevents transpiration. The olive is particularly important in 'Mediterranean' areas, and, in fact, it will not grow in any other kind of climate. Throughout the ages the oil from the fruit of the tree has been used by the people of these lands for a variety of purposes: for cooking-fat, sauce, soap, illuminant and lubricant.

The sunny summers are admirably suited to the ripening of fruit. Grape vines grow so well in the countries bordering the Mediterranean Sea that wine is very much cheaper than in England and is drunk almost as freely as water. Practically the entire world's supply of *citrus* fruit—that is oranges, lemons and other fruit with a thick waxy skin—comes from 'Mediterranean' areas.

In spite of the problem of summer drought, these regions have always provided a very attractive *habitat* (or place to live) for mankind. Man, like the plants, has learnt how to store up water to supply his needs through the dry period of the year, and from the very earliest times great civilisations have grown and flourished in the lands around the Mediterranean Sea. Until the discovery of America at the end of the fifteenth century, the Mediterranean was the 'centre' of the world in the sense that all the great advances in science and philosophy were made by Mediterranean peoples. Two obvious examples are provided by the Greeks and Romans. It is true that developments also took place in the monsoon lands of India and China. Since, however, these eastern lands were separated from the Mediterranean regions by a broad band of desert stretching from the

Sahara to the Gobi Desert of northern China, developments there occurred along rather different lines and were almost unknown to the peoples of the Mediterranean and the West. The historic background of western civilisation lies around the Mediterranean Sea.

It should be noted that the climate of the North Island of New Zealand is not quite the usual 'Mediterranean' type. Nor indeed is the natural vegetation of the North Island the same as that of other 'Mediterranean' areas; most of the trees and shrubs belong to the fern family (Fig. 200).

6. **Temperate Regions of Forest and Grassland.** The summer drought of the 'Mediterranean' lands is so remarkable a feature and so far-reaching in its consequences that it was convenient to consider the vegetation of the 'Mediterranean' areas in a separate section. In examining the vegetation of the remaining regions in temperate latitudes, we may more usefully consider them as a whole.

Fig. 200—Ferns near Auckland, New Zealand.

Whites Aviation, Ltd

The climatic conditions of the temperate regions tend to produce three main types of vegetation:

(i) Deciduous forest,
(ii) Coniferous forest,
(iii) Grassland.

Where the annual rainfall is 30 inches or more in amount and well distributed throughout the year, the natural vegetation is forest; in the warmer regions and where there are heavier soils, deciduous forest, and in the colder and higher parts and where the soils are lighter, coniferous forest.

Deciduous trees have more or less rounded outlines, the trunks are thick and the branches twisted. They take quite a long time to grow to maturity, in some cases, like the oak, hundreds of years. They have broad leaves, from the surface of which they transpire or breathe out the moisture sucked out of the ground by their roots, and they lose their leaves in autumn, or what Americans call the 'fall'. They are forced to shed their leaves in order to survive; if they did not do this, more water would be lost from the leaves by the cool breezes of winter than the tree could obtain from the ground (Fig. 201). Typical trees are the oak, elm, ash, beech and chestnut.

Coniferous trees are more triangular in shape, their trunks are thin and straight, and the branches are spaced fairly evenly

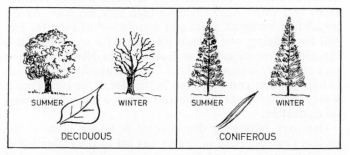

FIG. 201—A typical deciduous tree.　　FIG. 202—A typical coniferous tree.

on the trunk. The familiar Christmas tree is, in fact, a very young coniferous tree. They grow much more quickly than deciduous trees, and are often fully grown in fifteen to twenty years. In place of leaves coniferous trees have spines or needles, which remain on the trees throughout the year (Fig. 202). They are therefore classed as *evergreens*. The needles present to the atmosphere a much smaller surface than leaves would do, and the upward movement of water to the needles is therefore able to keep pace with transpiration. There are many varieties of coniferous trees, but the pine, spruce, larch and fir are perhaps the commonest.

Anyone who has travelled in Britain can see for himself how deciduous and coniferous trees are distributed in accordance with the above considerations. In the lowlands of southern England and the Midlands the majority of the trees are deciduous, except, for instance, in parts of Norfolk and Hampshire, where coniferous trees grow on patches of sandier soil. In the mountains of Wales and Scotland and in the Pennine uplands, where it is windier and colder, the trees are mainly of the coniferous type.

You will notice from the vegetation map of the world on p. 223 that the natural vegetation of the British Isles is classified as 'deciduous forest'. This is undoubtedly the kind of vegetation that Nature intended, and it is clear from records in the Domesday Book that areas of forest were in Norman times very much more extensive than they are now. As the population increased, more and more wood was cut for fuel and for building, and to clear the ground for agriculture. It is thought by historians that such areas as the New Forest were preserved only because medieval kings desired forests in which to hunt the deer and wild boar. In the case of the New Forest, it may also have been that the soils were too sandy for successful cultivation.

One very interesting development is taking place at the present time. Shortage of timber has led to the replanting of trees in many areas, and since coniferous timber is in general more useful than the wood from deciduous trees and will grow so much more quickly, the general appearance of much of our scenery is changing. Coniferous trees flourish in conditions suitable for deciduous trees, although the converse is not true, and the rounded outlines of groups of deciduous trees are gradually being replaced by stark and pointed shapes. Where forests in temperate regions have been cleared, grassland becomes the chief type of vegetation—a kind of grassland created and maintained by man rather than by Nature. This has happened not only in England, but also in many other parts of western Europe.

Vast areas of coniferous forest extend all the way across northern Canada and from Norway and Sweden into eastern Siberia. These cold, damp regions on the edge of the Tundra are sometimes referred to by their Russian name of *taïga*. They are of particular importance, since they represent the chief source of the world's softwood (commonly known as 'deal') for making all kinds of cheap crates and boxes, in addition to the wood pulp from which newsprint is made.

In interior continental situations, where rainfall is below 20 inches per annum and where in the warm summers a large proportion of the rainfall is evaporated, temperate grasslands prevail, to which in various parts of the world local names are given. In Canada these grasslands are known as *prairies*, in South America as *pampas*, in South Africa as *veldt*, in Russia as *steppes*, in Hungary as *pusztas* and in Australia as *downs*.

The soils of the temperate grasslands are usually rich and deep, and are very suitable for the large-scale production of wheat and other cereals, as, for instance, in the steppes of the Ukraine and the prairies of North America.

7. **Mountain Vegetation.** The vegetation of mountain areas depends on a number of varying factors, such as depth of soil, slope and aspect, but chiefly upon height and latitude. In temperate latitudes there is very little space below the snow-line to allow of the development of any vegetation differing greatly from that described in the previous section. In general, before the snow-line is reached, a zone of coniferous trees passes into scrubland and the scrubland into bare rock. In low latitudes,

however, the journey up a high mountain very much resembles a journey from the Equator to the Pole. The snow-line is, of course, much higher than it is in temperate regions and zones of savanna give place to deciduous forest, followed by coniferous forest and scrubland before the areas of perpetual snow are reached.

CHAPTER SEVENTEEN

Soils

THE FORMATION OF SOIL

THE soil in your garden and the sand on the seashore are both formed of fragments of disintegrated rock, but if you pick up a handful of sand, it will run away through your fingers, whereas the particles of soil will flocculate or cling together in groups. In this connection the term *crumb-structure* is used. You would not expect plants to grow in sand alone, but the soil, in addition to the rock fragments, contains various kinds of plant food in the form of compounds of sodium, calcium, potassium, nitrogen, phosphorus, carbon, etc., which have been added to the rock particles over the years by chemical changes due to the presence of air and water.

Soil also contains a certain amount of organic matter called *humus*, which is derived from the decayed remains of plants. Humus is a dark substance rather like the 'compost' which forms under a heap of grass cuttings, and is of the utmost importance in soil. It is another source of plant food, and also helps the other constituents of the soil to cling together.

As soon as the surface of the parent rock begins to break up under the influence of the forces of weathering, air and water enter into the spaces between the rock particles, and chemical changes begin to take place which make it possible for any stray seeds which find lodgment to grow into tiny plants. These plants die, their remains decay, and small quantities of humus form. This humus in turn makes it possible for more and more plants to grow, and microscopic organisms (called *bacteria*) start to work in what can now be termed the soil, and worms and other small creatures burrow in the ground and rearrange the particles. Thus an endless series of chemical and biological processes is set in motion.

They are, however, like most of the processes in Nature, very slow ones. It is probable that a thousand years or more must elapse to produce a foot of soil. If man in his folly allows the soil to deteriorate, and particularly if he allows the soil to be washed or blown away, it clearly is a very serious matter, since the world's food supply depends ultimately on there being available sufficiently large areas of the earth's surface on which crops can be grown. Fortunately, however, man is now not only alive to the dangers of allowing soils to be destroyed or removed, but is also becoming more capable of using his scientific knowledge to assist Nature.

THE FARMER'S CLASSIFICATION OF SOILS

Soils vary in many different ways, although the chief thing in which farmers throughout the ages have been interested is whether or not the soil is fertile. Generally speaking, a soil is fertile if it contains a sufficient amount of humus, but it is not really quite as simple as that. A soil in which one plant grows well may be quite unsuitable for another. It is important that it should contain the right chemical substances in the right proportions to suit a particular plant; moreover, a plant while taking from the soil the substances it requires for its own growth may also put into the soil substances required by other crops. Gardeners grow their cabbages and brussels sprouts in the patch of ground where peas and beans grew the previous year, and modern farmers know a great deal not only about the *rotation of crops*, by means of which they can prevent their soils from becoming exhausted, but also about the use of artificial fertilisers. The practice of 'muck-spreading' performs very much the same function in a far less scientific way.

The size of the grains has an important effect on the nature of a soil. If these are very small, as in clay, water will pass through the soil very slowly, and the farmer will speak of it as a *heavy* soil. The fact that it 'holds' the water so well will also prevent it warming up very quickly, and it may be described as a *cold* soil. If, on the other hand, the grains are comparatively large, as in sand, water will be able to pass quite rapidly through the spaces between the grains. Such a soil will be described as a *dry* or *sandy* soil, and since it will warm up quickly in summer, it can also be called a *warm* soil. A soil composed of a mixture of sand and clay is referred to as a *loam*.

One substance is of particular importance in soil—calcium carbonate or lime. It helps the other chemicals to do their work properly, and helps to 'lighten' or break up heavy ground. If there is not enough lime in the soil, it becomes *sour* or *acid.* When a gardener suspects that the soil on his allotment has become too acid, he spreads hydrated lime over the ground after the autumn digging. If he is a very keen gardener, he may take a sample of his soil to the local Horticultural Bureau and ask the officials there to analyse it and find out its pH value— in other words, to measure its acidity exactly, so that he will know precisely how much lime his ground requires. The term *marl* describes a soil consisting of a mixture of chalk and clay, but it is often used rather loosely.

THE GEOGRAPHER'S CLASSIFICATION OF SOILS

Until about fifty years ago, it was assumed that the nature of a soil depended directly on the parent rock from which it had been derived. It is now fairly clear that climate is much more important than the parent rock in producing a particular type of soil. The study of soils (*pedology*) has become a recognised branch of scientific enquiry, and, in addition to the rough and ready classification of soils used by the farmer, the geographer must know something of the latest discoveries in soil science.

The Soil Profile. If you are prepared to dig a deep enough hole in the ground or if you visit a quarry or railway cutting, you will certainly be able to detect three horizontal layers— first what we normally refer to as the 'soil', then the 'subsoil', and finally the 'solid rock' beneath. These three horizontal layers are called by the pedologist the *A* horizon, the *B* horizon and the *C* horizon respectively. A section showing the three horizons together is called the soil profile (Fig. 203), and examination of the depth, colour and chemical constituents of the horizons in various soil profiles all over the world has led to a classification of soils along these lines. This scientific classification is now extremely detailed, and it is only necessary here to describe some of the major types in order to illustrate the processes that lead to their formation.

Podzols. The two most important factors involved in forming the various types of soil profile are the movement of water in the soil and the temperature. In cool, wet conditions, such as are found in regions of coniferous forest, there is a general movement of water downwards. Minerals which are capable of being dissolved in the water are carried downwards and the *A* horizon is said to be *leached*. If this leaching is very extensive, the soil takes on a grey colour; lime will also be carried downwards in solution, and the soil becomes rather acid. Humus, lime and iron oxide tend to collect in the *B* horizon. If a large proportion of the humus is removed from the surface, the soil will lose its fertility, and iron oxide sometimes collects in sheets

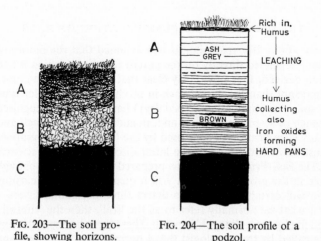

FIG. 203—The soil profile, showing horizons.

FIG. 204—The soil profile of a podzol.

forming an impermeable *hard pan*, so that the ground above becomes waterlogged. Soils displaying profiles of this character are known as podzols (Figs. 204 and 205). Podzol is a Russian word meaning 'ashen-grey soil'. Many of the names given to soil types are, in fact, of Russian origin, since the first attempts at classification were made by Russian scientists about ninety years ago.

Desert Soils. In dry climates the movement of water is upwards. Water in the ground rises by *capillarity*, and is evaporated from the surface. Minerals brought upwards in solution collect in the topmost part of the soil, which therefore becomes extremely salty. In some very dry climates the salts may form a crust on the surface. For example, *caliche* or Chile saltpetre forms a crust of this kind and is shovelled off and used to make fertiliser.

Brown Earth Soils. These are found under the climatic conditions which produce deciduous forest. They are rich in humus from the falling leaves, and are darker in colour and more fer-

Fig. 205—A soil profile of a podzol in the New Forest.

Eric Kay

240   *Soils*

tile than podzols, although a certain amount of leaching takes place.

Chernozems (or Black Earths). Some of the richest soils in the world are found in the temperate grasslands, and are known as chernozems or black earths. They derive their dark colour from the fact that while the grass provides a plentiful supply of humus, there is not sufficient rainfall to cause extensive leaching (Fig. 206).

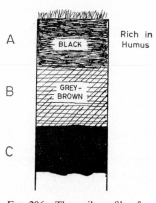

FIG. 206—The soil profile of a chernozem.

Chestnut Soils. These are akin to the chernozems, and occur principally on the drier fringes of the temperate grasslands where leaching is almost non-existent.

Tropical Red Earths. In tropical regions the soils are usually much deeper than in temperate regions. Great heat and moisture combine to break up the chemical compounds in the rock much more effectively than in cooler areas, and in what are known as tropical red earths large amounts of iron oxide are produced, which give the soils their characteristic red colour. Such soils are quite fertile when first cultivated, but their most valuable constituents are soon leached out. This is one of the reasons why native cultivators in, for example, Africa pass on from one patch of ground to another in the practice of shifting agriculture.

The above examples of the main soil types do not, of course, present anything like the complete picture. There are many others, with fascinating names like *terra rossa*, *rendzina* and *solonchak*, which we have no room to describe here. In America and in Great Britain a vast amount of survey work has been done in recent years, and numerous divisions and subdivisions have been made within the broad classification of *zonal soils* as first suggested by the Russians. Sufficient has, however, been said to show that, in the main, climate is the chief factor in the formation of the different kinds of soils, although the influence of the parent rock cannot always be disregarded. Limestone tends to produce its own special kinds of soil, but a wide variety of rocks has in separate regions given rise to chernozems.

It must also be realised that since soil formation is such a slow process, it takes a very long time for a *mature* soil with a well-marked profile to develop. *Young* soils formed on lava from comparatively recent volcanic eruptions, on alluvium deposited by rivers, on dust blown by the wind, or even on land reclaimed from the sea, as in the Netherlands, all form exceptions to the general rule.

One thing is, however, abundantly clear. The soil is one of Nature's most precious gifts to man. It is the most vital source of his food supply. Not only is the total world population increasing at an alarming rate, but also a tragically large proportion of the people in the world at present is considered to be under-fed. The more we understand about the natural processes which go on in the soil, the better able we shall be to make full use of Nature's gift.

EXAMINATION QUESTIONS

The following examination questions have been selected from a careful analysis of the papers set for the General Certificate of Education examinations at Ordinary Level by the various Examining Boards, who have kindly given permission to reproduce them. The Boards are indicated as follows: the University of Cambridge Local Examinations Syndicate (**C.**); the University of Durham (**D.**); the University of London (**L.**); the Northern Universities Joint Matriculation Board (**N.**); the University of Oxford Local Examinations Delegacy (**O.**); and

the Oxford and Cambridge Schools Examination Board
(**O. & C.**).

The questions are arranged more or less in the order of the
chapters; a strict division would be impossible, as many questions include more than one topic. Questions in which any
reference is made to topics outside the scope of this book, or
which are based on photographs, maps or charts supplied to
the candidate, have been excluded. This has necessarily involved the omission of a number of useful questions on, for
example, ocean currents, planetary winds and weather maps,
but avoids the inconvenience to the teacher of finding that
further equipment is required before certain of the questions
can be set as an exercise. The pupil should, however, note that
examining bodies almost always include questions involving
the explanation of physical features shown on photographs
and/or the insertion of geographical facts on blank maps.

The necessity for diagrams and sketch-maps in answering the
questions cannot be over-emphasised. Artistic ability is not required; it is sufficient that illustrative sketches should be reasonably large, clear, bold in outline, and should avoid irrelevant
detail. Printed lettering should be used on the diagrams, not
ordinary writing. With a little practice, it is not really difficult
to cultivate a clear, even style.

Citation of actual examples of features described is no less
important. Examples drawn from the pupil's own field-work
are particularly valuable.

One final point, though obvious, is often overlooked. The
pupil should familiarise himself with the precise meaning of
words and phrases commonly used in examination questions,
e.g. 'factor', 'development', 'locate', 'significance'.

1. With the aid of diagrams describe the appearance and
   probable formation of *three* of the following: volcano,
   range of 'young' fold mountains, barrier reef, horst. (**O.
   & C.**)
2. Choose *three* of the following features and explain, with
   the aid of diagrams, how each has been formed: block

mountain; fold mountain; residual mountain; volcanic mountain; escarpment. (**O.**)

3. Choose any *three* of the following: (i) alluvial plain; (ii) glaciated lowland; (iii) a young fold mountain system; (iv) a dissected plateau. For each one chosen (*a*) name and locate an example, (*b*) describe briefly its appearance and mode of formation. (**C.**)

4. Choose any *two* of the following: a barrier reef, a volcano, a delta. For each one you choose:
   (*a*) Describe its appearance.
   (*b*) Suggest how it was formed.
   (*c*) Locate an example by means of a sketch-map. (**C.**)

5. Describe, with the aid of diagrams, and explain the formation of *three* of the following, giving *one* example of each: volcanic plateau, flood plain, block mountain, lowland of denudation, boulder clay lowland. (**O. & C.**)

6. Explain the action and describe the results of the following in the formation of physical features: (*a*) mechanical weathering of rocks in cold climates, (*b*) chemical weathering of limestone, (*c*) wave action along deep-water coastlines. (**O. & C.**)

7. What are the physical characteristics of the *three* stages in the development of a river system? Quote actual examples. (**O.**)

8. EITHER—With the aid of diagrams and actual examples describe *three* common features to be found in and associated with the development of a river valley.
   OR—Describe *two* of the following and name an actual example of each. Illustrate your answer with contoured sketch-maps.
   (*a*) A drowned coast fringed with islands.
   (*b*) A glaciated valley in a highland region.
   (*c*) A typical chalk escarpment with gaps. (**L.**)

9. EITHER—(*a*) With the aid of diagrams and sketch-maps describe *three* of the following terms associated with the course of a river: delta, gorge, meanders, rapids, terrace.

OR—(*b*) Describe with the aid of diagrams and sketch-maps and name an actual example of the following coastal features: dune, lagoon, ria, stack, spit. (**L.**)

10. Illustrating your answer with diagrams, describe and account for the characteristic features of each of *three* of the following: wadi, middle course of a river valley, rift valley, canyon. (**O. & C.**)

11. If you were required to make a geographical study of a small river of *your own county*, describe the features you would look for and draw typical diagrams which you would use to illustrate your study. Give examples of such features from your knowledge of a particular locality. (**D.**)

12. EITHER—Select *two* of the following and for each name an example and draw a carefully numbered contoured sketch-map:

   (*a*) a U-shaped valley with a hanging tributary valley,
   (*b*) an escarpment with a dissected dip slope and a gap,
   (*c*) a coastline with two cliffed promontories separated by a sandy bay.

   OR—Describe with examples and diagrams *three* ways in which mountains are formed. (**L.**)

13. Choose *three* of the following: karst scenery, river capture, fjord, rift valley, canyon. Give an example of each of the three you choose and explain how it has been formed. (**O.**)

14. EITHER—With the aid of well-labelled diagrams or sketch-maps, describe *three* characteristic features of a glaciated valley in a highland area and name *three* highland areas which have been glaciated.

   OR—With the aid of well-labelled diagrams or sketch-maps describe the formation and name an actual example of *three* of the following: artesian basin, canyon, crater lake, delta, sand spit. (**L.**)

15. Illustrating your answer with diagrams, describe and explain the development of the physical features which result from the action of water in (*a*) limestone areas, (*b*) highland areas of hard old rock. (**O. & C.**).

16. Choose *three* of the following features: a glaciated lowland; a coral reef; a surf-bound coast; an area of artificial drainage; a limestone gorge. For each selected feature name and locate a particular example and describe how it has been formed. (**D.**)

17. The following features are associated with glaciation: cirque or corrie, hanging valley, moraine dammed lake, pyramidal peak. Select *three* of these features, and for *each* describe with the aid of a diagram how it is formed and locate an example. (**L.**)

18. EITHER—With the aid of clearly labelled diagrams describe *three* of the following associated with glaciation: corrie (cirque or cwm), hanging valley, morainic hills, U-shaped valley, waterfall.
    OR—Describe, with the aid of carefully labelled diagrams, *three* ways in which a lake may be formed. Locate an actual example of *each*. (**L.**)

19. Name and locate *three* of the following features: gorge, lake, pass, ria. For each of your chosen examples,

    (*a*) explain how it has been formed;
    (*b*) state its geographical importance. (**D.**)

20. Select *four* different types of coastline. Name a locality where each is to be found, and explain how it has been formed. (**O.**)

21. Choose *three* of the following: a ria coastline, a haff coastline, a fjord, a coral reef. For each (i) state the location of a particular example; (ii) explain and illustrate by diagrams how such a feature has been formed. (**N.**)

22. Select *three* of the following: Germany east of the Oder, the south-west of South Island New Zealand, Jugoslavia, south-eastern U.S.A. For each area chosen, with the aid of a diagram, describe and account for the physical features of the coast. (**O. & C.**)

23. Name *three* great fishing grounds of the world excluding the area around the British Isles. What are the conditions present in any *one* of them which explain the abundance

of fish? Why are there no great fishing grounds in the tropics? (**O.**)

24. By reference in each case to a specific example, describe the characteristic features of *two* of the following: a coral reef, an area of volcanic activity, a chalk upland, a glaciated valley. Draw sketch-maps to show the location of each example chosen and illustrate your answer by diagrams. (**N.**)

25. With the aid of sketch-maps and diagrams give an explanatory account of each of *three* of the following: the Benguela current, the degree of salinity in the Red Sea, the continental shelf, an atoll. (**O. & C.**)

26. With the aid of diagrams explain the formation of: (*a*) relief rain, (*b*) convectional rain, (*c*) cyclonic rain. (**O. & C.**)

27. (*a*) Describe an instrument used to measure the pressure of the atmosphere, and say how you would record the information obtained by using this instrument; (*b*) suggest reasons why there tends to be high pressure over continents in winter and low pressure in summer. (**C.**)

28. State clearly what you understand by *three* of the following terms and show their importance in weather study: (*a*) anticyclones; (*b*) a Warm Front; (*c*) temperature inversion; (*d*) relative humidity. (**C.**)

29. Give an actual example and explain with the aid of diagrams *three* of the following: a low-pressure system, convectional rainfall, monsoon winds, rain shadow. (**L.**)

30. Explain the following:

    (*a*) In England the period of daylight is longer on 21st June than on 21st December.

    (*b*) On the Equator periods of daylight and darkness are always equal.

    (*c*) At the Poles the sun does not set for many weeks on end in one part of the year.

    (*d*) On two occasions in the year day and night are equal all over the earth. (**O.**)

31. Explain the causes of summer and winter seasons. (**O.**)

32. Explain, using diagrams:

      (i) Why temperature changes with latitude.
      (ii) What effect relief has on rainfall.
      (iii) Why December days are long in New Zealand but short in Britain. (**L.**)

33. Illustrating your answer with diagrams, give an explanatory account of the type of rainfall commonly experienced in (*a*) equatorial lands, (*b*) eastern England in winter, (*c*) southern Chile. (**O. & C.**)

34. (*a*) Locate on sketch-maps the areas in the world which experience a Mediterranean climate; (*b*) describe the characteristics of the natural vegetation of these areas and show how they are related to the climate. (**O. & C.**)

35. Draw a simple sketch-map to show the west coast of *one* continent and mark on it *three* areas, each of which experiences a different type of climate. Describe each of the three types of climate. (**C.**)

36. The following data refer to towns *A* and *B* which are near sea-level:

	Jan.	Feb.	Mar.	Apr.	May	June	July	Aug.	Sept.	Oct.	Nov.	Dec.
Town A °F.	55	56	57	61	65	70	73	75	72	66	61	56
Rainfall ins.	5·1	4·2	4·8	2·7	1·7	0·5	0·0	0·1	1·4	3·3	6·4	5·5
Town B °F.	61	61	59	55	50	47	45	46	49	52	55	59
Rainfall ins.	10·0	7·4	9·7	9·2	9·8	9·8	9·1	9·2	9·3	11·7	10·6	10·4

(*a*) On the graph paper provided show the relative annual distribution of temperatures for the two towns.

(*b*) Describe the seasonal distribution of rainfall at (i) *A*, (ii) *B*, and for each state the type of climate.

(*c*) Suggest, with reasons, a possible location for each town. (**D.**)

37. Describe and account for the main features of the climate of *two* of the following: Egypt, the Congo Basin, Northern Australia. (**C.**)

38. Describe, with the aid of diagrams, the variety of weather experienced during the passage of a depression over any part of western Europe during the summer months. (**O.**)

39. (a) On separate sketch-maps locate *one* area of equatorial forest and *one* area of coniferous forest; (b) for the areas located state *three* differences in each of the following:

    (i) their natural vegetations and
    (ii) their climates. (**L.**)

40. Describe and account for the succession of vegetation regions on the west coast of *one* of the following: Africa north of the Equator, Africa south of the Equator, South America (**L.**)

41. Describe the principal characteristics of each of *three* of the following types of natural vegetation: savanna, monsoon forest, temperate deciduous forest, tundra. Show how each type chosen is related to the climate of one area in which it is found. (**O. & C.**)

42. Draw separate sketch-maps to locate an important area of each of (a) savanna vegetation, and (b) temperate grassland. Describe each type of natural vegetation and show clearly how it is related to the climate of the area. (**C.**)

43. (a) Describe (i) the natural forest of an equatorial lowland; (ii) the deciduous forest of a temperate lowland.
    (b) State the chief ways in which these forests differ. (**C.**)

44. Describe and account for the different types of natural vegetation which might be seen on a journey from the Caspian Sea to the Arctic coast. (**C.**)

45. Compare the natural vegetation of the temperate maritime and Mediterranean regions, illustrating your answer with actual examples. (**L.**)

46. Account for (a) the marked summer rainfall maximum in the valleys of (i) the Ganges, (ii) the Orinoco; (b) the low average rainfall on the coasts of (i) Peru, (ii) Arctic Canada. (**O. & C.**)

47. Select *three* of the following: alluvium, boulder-clay, shingle beach, loess, peaty soil. For each: (a) name and locate an actual example; (b) describe how it has been formed. (**D.**)

Index

Index